PERGAMON OXFORD GEOGRAPHIES

General Editor: W. B. FISHER

A Geography of the Soviet Union

A Geography
of the Soviet Union

by

JOHN C. DEWDNEY, M.A. (EDIN.)

Professor of Geography at Fourah Bay College,
the University College of Sierra Leone.
Sometime Lecturer in Geography in the University of Durham

PERGAMON PRESS

OXFORD · LONDON · EDINBURGH · NEW YORK
TORONTO · PARIS · FRANKFURT

Pergamon Press Ltd., Headington Hill Hall, Oxford
4 & 5 Fitzroy Square, London W.1
Pergamon Press (Scotland) Ltd., 2 & 3 Teviot Place, Edinburgh 1
Pergamon Press Inc., 44–01 21st Street, Long Island City, New York 11101
Pergamon of Canada Ltd., 6 Adelaide Street East, Toronto, Ontario
Pergamon Press S.A.R.L., 24 rue des Écoles, Paris 5^e
Pergamon Press GmbH, Kaiserstrasse 75, Frankfurt-am-Main

Printed in Great Britain by Cheltenham Press Ltd., Cheltenham

CONTENTS

LIST OF FIGURES

LIST OF TABLES

EDITOR'S FOREWORD

AT the present time there is no need to explain or justify a choice of the Soviet Union as a subject for geographical study. Yet in spite of the significance of the U.S.S.R. as a major world power we possess very few books in English that offer a comprehensive and overall view of Russian geography within the compass of a small-scale text usable by senior pupils in schools. Over the last few years there have appeared a number of large-scale studies of the Soviet Union, but these have been either in greater part for reference or else designed in style and treatment, for the relatively advanced student.

It is the aim of Mr. Dewdney's book to present the salient geographical elements of the contemporary U.S.S.R. for pupils in schools, at fifth- and sixth-form level, and as an outline or introductory text for first year university students. Moreover, a feature in many schools and universities is the increasing attention given to geography as part of the background to studies of language and literature; and it is hoped that the present work will thus also be of use to the small but growing numbers who study Russian as a major language.

Reflecting possibly what has now become a trend in certain university Geography departments—and undoubtedly the case in Durham—the author's treatment is on a systematic basis, by topic rather than by region. Whilst appropriate consideration is given to physical elements, there is somewhat more extended treatment of economic aspects. This is perhaps only proper in dealing with the U.S.S.R. Regions as such are discussed, but on a minor scale, since in the opinion of some geographers, the subject is now in the process of moving to consideration of conditions and problems—human, economic and political—posed by the various geographical features, with regions an incidental, though not negligible, factor. The traditional method in geography, that of erecting regional subdivision as a dominant element must thus be replaced by new treatment. Natural regions and associated concepts have for long been a useful approach and a sound framework, but more advanced ideas are now necessary, since growth of modern communications has in some ways destroyed what we can call traditional regional units, and the activities of man are creating at accelerating speed new situations, new human groupings, new problems and opportunities. All these to some extent render outdated the idea of a fixed regional pattern delimited by physical features. It is now the function of modern geography to offer an assessment of the part played by environment in fostering and influencing not only these changes but their resulting challenges in human existence. For few areas can this be better seen than in the Soviet Union.

Mr. Dewdney has first-hand experience of those parts of the U.S.S.R. that a foreigner may visit. His study attempts to show how human ingenuity and activity have transformed a major segment of the earth's surface, despite the handicaps imposed by great distances, a harsh climate, and by a turbulent historical past both within and on the frontiers of Russia, that has produced revolution, devastation and consequent slowness in development. This is why such topics as territorial administration and transport are regarded as sufficiently important to have separate chapters; and why there are no chapter headings on a purely regional basis.

Statistics are not always easy to come by or sufficiently informative when obtained; and comparison on a basis of proportion may not always convey the real position, even though its arithmetic can be wholly sound. In terms of economic development, it is a very different matter to increase by 50 per cent or even double an activity that is in its first stages, as compared with one that is already a large and efficient producer. To double one only adds another one; whereas doubling a thousand involves effort on a totally different scale. This tendency to compare by proportional growth leads to some difficulty both within the U.S.S.R., where there are some areas in an early stage of growth and others much more advanced, and also when Russian achievements are set alongside those of other countries. Nevertheless, sufficient statistics are now available to allow a better and more detailed picture of developments in the Soviet Union than we in the West often appreciate, and it will be obvious that the present book is based wherever possible on actual facts and figures rather than upon impressions or comparison. Objective knowledge of the U.S.S.R. has so far been rather lacking in our schools and universities—for many reasons we should know more of this interesting, remarkable and different country.

W. B. FISHER

PREFACE

CONTACTS with teachers in schools and universities who are concerned with teaching the geography of the Soviet Union have convinced me that there is a real need for a compact, up-to-date, systematic treatment of the subject, which will provide basic information and serve as a starting point for further study. Such are the intentions of this book.

Figures 3 and 5 are based on maps appearing on pages 10 and 13 of *The Economic Geography of the U.S.S.R.* by Bal'zak, Vasyutin and Feigin, copyright, 1959, by the American Council of Learned Societies, used with permission of the Macmillan Company. Figure 33 is based on a map by R. E. Lonsdale and J. H. Thompson appearing in *Economic Geography*, **36**, no. 1, Jan. 1960, p. 42, with the authors' and editors' permission.

I should like to express my thanks to Mr. G. McWhirter, who prepared the final drawings for many of the illustrations and to Miss S. J. Pennington who typed the manuscript. I should also like to place on record my gratitude to Professor W. B. Fisher for his constant help and encouragement.

Durham　　　　　　　　　　　　　　　　　　　　　　　JOHN C. DEWDNEY
April 1964

INTRODUCTION

THE most obvious yet at the same time one of the most significant facts about the Soviet Union is its enormous size. The country covers an area of 22·4 million sq km (8·6 million sq miles) approximately one-sixth of the earth's land surface. From the western frontier to the Bering Strait is a distance of nearly 10,000 km (6000 miles) and the maximum latitudinal extent, from the Arctic Ocean to the borders of Afghanistan is 4800 km (over 3000 miles). No other political unit in the world approaches the size of the U.S.S.R., which is more than twice as large as China, nearly three times as big as the United States or Australia, and no less than ninety-three times the size of the United Kingdom (Fig. 1). However, the population of the Soviet Union, which on 1 January 1962 stood at 220 million, is a good deal less impressive than its area, being greatly exceeded by those of China (700 million) and India (440 million). The United States has 186 million

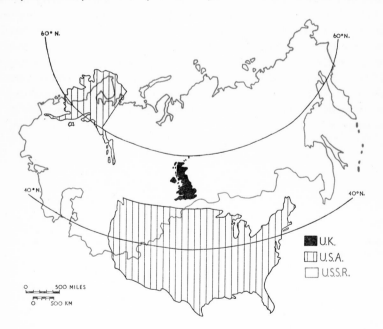

FIG. 1. A comparison of the relative sizes of the U.K., U.S.A., and U.S.S.R. The three countries are shown in their correct latitudinal positions.

inhabitants. The overall population density in the U.S.S.R. is approximately 10 per sq km (25 per sq mile), less than half the world average. This low figure suggests another important fact the reasons for which will become apparent as we proceed, namely that a great deal of the Soviet Union is very thinly peopled; much of it can be described as virtually uninhabited. While this state of affairs is largely a result of the very harsh physical environment which exists over large areas, there are at the same time considerable stretches of territory which could, and no doubt eventually will, support much larger numbers of people than they do at present.

A country of such enormous size must be expected to have a great variety of physical conditions within its boundaries and this is certainly the case with the Soviet Union. At the same time, the individual physical regions are so large that monotonous uniformity of landscape over wide areas is as characteristic as the great contrasts between one region and another. To variety in the various aspects of physical geography must be added variety in the racial, historical and cultural backgrounds of the people and in their way of life. The contrasts between the sophisticated town-dwellers of Moscow, Leningrad and other great cities of European Russia and the nomadic pastoralists of Soviet Central Asia or the primitive tribes of the Arctic are as great as those between, say, the Londoner and the inhabitant of Persia or Alaska. Despite the rapid and far-reaching changes which have taken place in the Soviet Union over the past forty-five years, these contrasts still exist; indeed in some ways they have become more marked, since modern economic development, particularly in the industrial sphere, has affected some areas to a much greater extent than others. The existence of a highly centralized political and economic system with clearly defined aims and methods of operation applied to the country as a whole should not blind us to the great diversity of conditions, physical and human, which exist within the boundaries of the Soviet Union.

GEOLOGY

QUATERNARY	MESOZOIC
TERTIARY	PALEOZOIC

ARCHAEAN	
INTRUSIVE	

LIMIT OF MAXIMUM (RISS) GLACIATION

MILES   1000

KILOMETRES   1000
0

FIG. 2. Simplified geological map.

CHAPTER 1

STRUCTURE AND RELIEF

IT IS not possible in a book of this size to give a full and detailed account of the geological structure of the Soviet Union (Fig. 2) and in this chapter our attention must be concentrated on the main relief features. Nevertheless, some knowledge of the basic structural elements is necessary and these are best understood if we recall the main features of the structure of the world as a whole. Basically, there are two major elements, stable blocks or "continental platforms" and orogenic belts or zones of mountain building. The continental platforms are composed of extremely tough igneous and metamorphic rocks which were formed at great depth beneath the surface during mountain-building episodes in very early (Archaean or pre-Cambrian) geological times. These hard materials have proved resistant to all later fold movements and, although they have been faulted, raised and lowered *en masse* by epeirogenic earth movements and subjected to long periods of sub-aerial denudation, their structures are quite different from those of the intervening orogenic belts. The latter are zones of the earth's crust where, on various occasions, great thicknesses of sedimentary rocks, derived from the denudation of adjacent "platforms", have been thrown into folds by vigorous lateral orogenic or mountain-building earth movements.

The Soviet Union contains two stable blocks, the East European and Siberian platforms, between and around which have developed fold mountain systems from each of the major orogenic periods, the Caledonian, Hercynian, Mesozoic and Alpine. The distribution of these elements is shown on the map of tectonic zones (Fig. 3). This map divides the Soviet Union into zones according to the geological period during which the last main folding took place. Thus, in the area marked pre-Cambrian (Archaean), there has been little folding since the pre-Cambrian era, in that marked Caledonian there has been little since the Caledonian orogeny and so on. It will be observed that these tectonic zones do not in every case correspond with the relief regions indicated in Fig. 4. This is because, at the present time, structures formed in the earlier periods are not everywhere visible at the surface. In many areas they have been worn down by denudation and covered by younger sedimentary rocks which lie nearly horizontally and remain at low elevations above sea-level. The Ural Mountains and the West Siberian Lowland, for example, are both part of the Hercynian zone because

1

folding took place in both these areas in Hercynian times. However, the Hercynian structures of the West Siberian Lowland are buried beneath younger
sedimentaries, while those of the Urals are exposed at the surface, so that the two
regions, while they are parts of the same *structural* zone, are quite different in
their *relief*. The map of tectonic zones therefore distinguishes areas in which the
structures of the periods named are exposed at or near the surface from areas
where they are buried beneath later materials.

TECTONIC ZONES

1a 1b   2a 2b   3a 3b   4   5

AFTER BALZAK, VASYUTIN & FEIGIN

MILES   1000

KILOMETRES   1000

FIG. 3. Tectonic zones. 1a: Archaean (exposed); 1b: Archaean (concealed); 2a:
Caledonian (exposed); 2b: Caledonian (concealed); 3a: Hercynian (exposed); 3b:
Hercynian (concealed); 4: Mesozoic; 5 Alpine. For explanation, see text. (Based
on a map appearing on page 10 of *Economic Geography of the U.S.S.R.* by S. S.
Bal'zak, V. F. Vasyutin and Y. G. Feigin. Copyright 1949 by the American
Council of Learned Societies. Used with permission of the Macmillan
Company.)

The general arrangement is fairly simple. There are, as already indicated,
two pre-Cambrian platforms, the East European and the Siberian. Major areas
of Caledonian folding are found in association with the latter, one belt occurring
on its south-western side and another running in a south-west to north-east
direction which cuts the Siberian platform into two parts. Hercynian structures
occupy a wide area between the two platforms while belts of Mesozoic and
Alpine folding run along the southern side of the East European platform, the
Hercynian zone and the Siberian platform and continue around the eastern edge
of the latter.

RELIEF

LAND ABOVE 1000 METRES

LAND ABOVE 200 METRES

MILES   1000

KILOMETRES   1000

FIG. 4. Generalized relief map.

THE EAST EUROPEAN PLATFORM

This occupies the bulk of the Soviet Union west of the Urals, but the resistant rocks of which it is composed outcrop at the surface over very limited parts of the area: the **Fenno-Scandian** or Baltic Shield in the north and the **Podol'sk-Azov** or Ukrainian Shield in the south. Elsewhere, the ancient rocks are covered by younger sedimentaries. The thickness of the sedimentary cover varies a great deal since the underlying platform has been considerably warped and faulted, and the surface rocks become progressively younger from north to south. The relief of this area, the **East European Plain,** is extremely gentle. Only in a very few places do heights exceed 1000 ft (300 m) and even land above 500 ft (150 m) is very limited in extent. A large part of the plain was affected by the Pleistocene glaciation and features of glacial deposition occur widely. In a region of this sort, small differences in height assume considerable importance and a number of distinct relief features, several of them of glacial origin, may be observed.

The Russian section of the **Baltic Shield** occupies the area between the Gulf of Finland and the White Sea, extending northward into the **Kolskiy Poluostrov** (Kola Peninsula). Here, the ancient rocks are exposed at the surface and, although the relief is low, the area was near the centre of ice dispersion and shows features of glacial erosion. The surface has been swept bare of superficial deposits, but at the same time glacial drift accumulated in hollows so that there is an alternation of bare, ice-scraped rock with shallow depressions which often contain lakes and marshes. The greatest altitudes, over 3000 ft (900 m), are reached in a few places in the **Khibiny Khrebet** (Khibin Mountains), but the bulk of this region lies well below 1000 ft (300 m).

The Baltic Shield is bounded on its southern side by a faulted trough which contains the Gulf of Finland, **Ladozhskoye Ozero** and **Onezhskoye Ozero** (Lakes Ladoga and Onega). South of this trough, the sedimentary rocks of the East European Plain begin. Here, Paleozoic materials dip south and south-eastwards towards the **Moscow Basin,** and have been eroded to give a series of escarpments and intervening lowlands. The most prominent scarp is that formed by the Carboniferous limestone which gives rise to the **Valdayskaya Vozvyshennost'** (Valday Hills), running in a north-east to south-west direction from the southern end of Onezhskoye Ozero (Lake Onega) to the northern frontier of the Belorussian Republic. These hills appear to have acted as a temporary barrier to ice movement and are capped by a moraine which raises their height to a maximum of 1138 ft (347 m). At one stage in the ice retreat, drainage north-westward from the Valdayskaya Vozvyshennost' (Valday Hills) was blocked by the ice front and large pro-glacial lakes accumulated between the glacier and rising ground. **Il'men' Ozero** (Lake Ilmen) is a remnant of one such lake. Another morainic ridge of considerable importance is the **Smolensko-Moskovskaya Vozvyshennost'** (Smolensk – Moscow Ridge), which runs in a north-easterly direction to pass just north of the capital. This zone of morainic ridges and large pro-glacial lakes is confined to the area covered by ice during the most recent of the four major advances which affected the region, that of the *Würm* period. Here, as elsewhere in Europe, the Pleistocene ice-age involved four advances of the continental ice-sheets, known respectively as the *Gunz*, *Mindel*, *Riss* and *Würm* periods, and these were separated by inter-glacial phases. The ice-sheets reached their greatest extent during the *Riss* advance and the final, *Würm*, advance reached only to the approximate latitude of Moscow. North of the line marking the maximum extent of the *Würm* ice-sheet, the features of glacial deposition are very fresh and have been relatively little modified by post-glacial normal erosion. South of this dividing line, however, though features of glacial origin are by no means absent they are much less clearly marked and the pre-glacial relief is more readily visible. South of the latitude of Moscow, there is an east–west alternation of low plateaux and still lower valley plains. The **Sredny Russkaya Vozvyshennost'** (Central Russian Elevation) rises to a maximum of 940 ft (286 m) above sea-level and marks the south-western edge of the Moscow Basin. The plateau is bounded on its western side by the plains of the upper Dnepr and on the east by those of the upper Don. The latter in turn give way eastward to the **Privolzhskaya Vozvyshennost'** (pre-Volga Heights). This arrangement affected the movement of the *Riss* ice-sheet (older but more extensive than that of the *Würm*) which sent lobes of ice down the two valleys but left most of the Central Elevation and pre-Volga Heights clear of ice. The features resulting from deposition by the *Riss* ice-sheet have been largely removed by river action or covered by fluvio-glacial outwash *loess* and *limon* laid down south of the *Würm* ice-front. However, the lowlands of the upper Dnepr and Don were areas in which large quantities of glacial melt-water accumulated and they remain very poorly drained. This is particularly the case in the **Poles'ye** or Pripet Marsh area.

Still further south, the presence of the Ukrainian Shield is reflected in the surface relief. The Archaean rocks reach the surface over a considerable part of the western Ukraine in the area known as the **Volyno-Podol'skaya Vozvy-shennost'** (Volyno-Podol'sk Upland). This plateau diminishes in height eastwards across the Dnepr, but rises again to 1066 ft (325 m) in the **Priazov-skaya Vozvyshennost'** (pre-Azov Heights). The whole area is covered with *loess* or *limon*. Topographically, but not structurally, the Priazovskaya Vozvy-shennost' are continuous with the **Donetskiy Kryazh** (Donetz Heights) which lie to the north-east. The latter, however, represent an area lying just north of the Ukrainian Shield in which the Archaean rocks are far below the surface and a great thickness of sedimentary materials (including Carboniferous deposits) were folded in Hercynian and again in Mesozoic times. The resultant ridges in places reach 1200 ft (366 m) above sea-level.

South of the Ukrainian Massif, broad, gently-sloping plains of *loess*-covered

Tertiary sediments reach into the south-west Ukraine and the Crimean peninsula, where they are terminated by the Tertiary fold mountains of the Crimean range. In the **Azov–Caspian Depression,** the surface rocks are of Quaternary age.

The eastern section of the plain must now be considered, though in a little less detail. The major uplands are the **Timanskiy Kryazh** (Timan Range), a Caledonian fold system extending north-westward from the Urals to the Arctic Ocean, and the **Ufa Plateau,** a *horst* block on the western side of the Ural ranges. The bulk of the remainder of the area is composed of near-horizontal sedimentary rocks among which the Permian is the most widespread outcrop. This zone is drained in the north by the Severnaya Dvina (Northern Dvina) river system and in the south by the Kama–Volga. While the former is an area of widespread glacial deposition, the latter for the most part escaped glaciation since the ice-sheets halted further north here than in the west. These eastern areas, which form the most monotonous part of the European plain give way in the south to broad expanses of Quaternary lowland which extend north of the Caspian and mark the former limits of that sea.

URAL'SKIY KHREBET (THE URAL MOUNTAINS)

During the Paleozoic era, a depression developed in the earth's crust between the European and Siberian platforms. In this depression were deposited great thicknesses of sedimentary rocks derived from erosion of the East European and Siberian platforms to the west and east respectively. At the end of the Paleozoic, these sediments were thrown into folds by the Hercynian earth-movements and a vast mountain-system came into being, stretching from the site of the present Urals to the Yenisey River. Sub-aerial denudation eventually reduced the whole area to a peneplane but in Tertiary times a relatively narrow western strip of territory was re-elevated and it is the subsequent erosion of this strip which has produced the present landforms of the Urals. The modern Ural Mountains thus represent only a small fraction of the Hercynian orogenic belt and owe their height to the Tertiary uplift and not to the original folding.

It is common practice to distinguish three subdivisions of the Urals. The **Severnyy Ural** (Northern Urals), extending from the Arctic Ocean to latitude 58°N., are the narrowest part of the system and consist of a single major ridge with subsidiary ridges parallel to it. The main ridge is composed of resistant materials and heights above 5000 ft (1500 m) are reached in a few places. The **Sredniy Ural** (Central Urals), between latitudes 58° and 55°N., are developed on weaker rocks and are much lower, with a maximum height of only 2600 ft (800 m). In the **Yuzhnyy Ural** (Southern Urals), the system is a good deal wider than in either the centre or the north and comprises a series of ridges and valleys which fan out towards the south. One of these ridges contains the highest point in the whole system at 5370 ft (1638 m).

Despite their role as the traditional boundary between Europe and Asia, the Urals are in no way a serious barrier to movement between the two sections of the country. Maximum heights of little more than 5000 ft (1500 m) are by no means impressive and the system takes the form of a series of parallel ridges separated by longitudinal depressions and broken by transverse valleys. As a result, low passes are plentiful, particularly in the central section which has long been the main gateway from Europe to Siberia. The importance of the Urals, as we shall see later, lies in their rich mineral resources which occur where ancient rocks have been exposed at the surface by long periods of erosion.

ZAPADNO-SIBIRSKAYA NIZMENNOST' (THE WEST SIBERIAN LOWLAND)

This is the most remarkable single relief feature in the Soviet Union. For a distance of a thousand miles (1600 km) from the Urals to the Yenisey, and for over 1200 miles (1900 km) from north to south, the land never rises more than 600 ft (180 m) above sea-level. The Paleozoic basement, with its Hercynian structures, is buried by younger sedimentary rocks to depths as great as 5000 ft (1500 m). The area has been submerged for long periods on several occasions since the Paleozoic era and the sediments are everywhere horizontal or extremely gently tilted. By far the greater part of the surface is composed of Quaternary materials and only in the south-west, towards the border of Kazakhstan, are Tertiary rocks at all widespread. However, the Quaternaries vary a good deal in their composition. In the south, they include fluvio-glacial and *loess* deposits laid down beyond the margins of the ice-sheet; in the centre they are largely morainic; in the north they are marine, the product of an extensive advance of the sea in post-glacial times.

The region as a whole is extremely poorly drained, having a very gentle northward slope, and there are large areas of marsh and bog as well as innumerable lakes. The rivers, of which the Yenisey, Ob' and Irtyish are the most important, are wide and slow-flowing. Their shallow valleys are as much as 75 miles (120 km) across in places and the flood plains are up to 25 miles (40 km) in width. The south-western Tertiary zone is appreciably drier for climatic as well as topographic reasons, and it is here that the bulk of the settlement and agricultural land is to be found.

KAZAKHSKIY MELKOSOPOCHNIK (THE KAZAKH UPLAND)

This region borders the West Siberian Lowland on its southern side. Like the Urals, it is an area which was folded in Hercynian times, reduced to a peneplane by sub-aerial denudation and re-elevated in more recent geological times so that it now consists of a series of plateaux and low hill-ranges. The highest elevations, about 4700 ft (1400 m), are found in the centre of the region, but the greater part lies between 1500 and 3000 ft (450–900 m). Although in places a few patches of Mesozoic materials have been preserved, most of the surface is composed either of Paleozoic sedimentaries or pre-Cambrian metamorphic and igneous rocks. The ancient rocks have been exposed by long-continued de-nudation and are often very rich in minerals. The Kazakh Upland lies in the semi-desert and desert zones and permanent surface water is rare.

TURANSKAYA NIZMENNOST'
(THE TURANIAN (OR TURKESTAN) LOWLAND)

The Kazakh Upland is connected to the southern Urals by the **Turġayskaya Stolovaya Strana** (Turgay Plateau), an area of horizontally-bedded Tertiary materials standing between 600 and 900 ft (180–270 m) above sea-level. Through the centre of the plateau runs a narrow corridor, the **Turġayskiye Vorota** (Turgay Gate), which forms a link, below 300 ft (90 m), between the West Siberian and Turanian Lowlands. The latter, which occupies the greater part of Soviet Central Asia, is continuous, on its western side, with the Caspian Lowland, but is closed in on the north, east and south by the Urals, the Kazakh Upland and the young fold-mountain systems. Apart from the areas close to the Caspian which are, of course, below world sea-level the most low-lying districts are found around the **Aral'skoye More** (Aral Sea). The largest rivers of the region, the Amu-Dar'ya and the Syr-Dar'ya, flow from the southern mountains into this sea which is the centre of a closed system of inland drainage. Several sizeable rivers, the Sarysu and the Chu, for example, disappear into the desert without even reaching the centre of the basin. The Aral Sea is a fairly shallow water-body: though the greatest depth is rather more than 200 ft (60 m), most of it is less than 100 ft (30 m) deep. A second centre of inland drainage with a much smaller catchment area is provided by **Ozero Balkhash** (Lake Balkhash), whose average depth is only about 20 ft (6 m).

A number of contrasting physiographic regions go to make up the **Turanskaya Nizmennost'**. Tertiary outcrops give rise to a number of low plateaux with steep, scarped edges where they overlook the more low-lying Quaternary areas. The **Plato Ustyurt** (Ust-Urt Plateau) stands at heights of 500–700 ft (150–210m) between the Caspian and Aral Seas and is continued southward by the **Krasnovodskoye Plato** (Krasnovodsk Plateau), which in places reaches 1000 ft (300 m). The **Bet–Pak–Dala Plato**, between the southern edge of the Kazakh Upland and the Syr-Dar'ya River is largely between 900 and 1100 ft (270–330 m) above sea-level.

The Turanian Lowland lies within the semi-desert and desert zones, mostly in the latter, and desert landforms predominate over the greater part of it. These are most clearly seen in a number of large sand deserts, which include the area south of Lake Balkhash, the **Peski Muyun–Kum** between the Chu River and the southern mountains, the **Peski Kyzyl-Kum** between the Syr-Dar'ya and Amu-Dar'ya and the **Peski Kara-Kum** between the latter river and the Caspian. In all these areas sand dunes, largely fixed by a scanty vegetation cover, alternate with clayey depressions where, because of surface accumulations of salt, vegetation is virtually absent.

The valleys of the major rivers form another distinctive region, with numerous river terraces and broad alluvial flood plains. These together with the basins lying between the southern mountain ranges offer great potentialities for the development of irrigated agriculture.

THE SIBERIAN PLATFORM

This is a zone in which structures are particularly complex and where relationships between structure and relief are by no means simple. It will be seen from the map of tectonic zones (Fig. 3) that the platform is divided into two parts by a belt of Caledonian folding which affected lower Paleozoic sediments laid down in a deep trough developed across the platform. To the west and north-west of this Caledonian belt is the **Anabar Shield.** Archaean materials are exposed at the surface over a small area in the north, but elsewhere lie deeply buried under sedimentary rocks. In the north-eastern part of the shield, and thence southwards to the upper Lena, these are lower Paleozoic in age, but over a wide area in the west they become much thicker and range from lower Paleozoic to Permian, the latter outcropping over a very large area in the **Tunguska** (Tungus Basin). The relief of this part of Siberia, however, bears little relation to the structural arrangement just described. The **Sredne-Sibirskoye Ploskogor'ye** (Central Siberian Plateau) is in fact a series of plateaux at various heights between 1000 and 2500 ft (300–750 m), developed indiscriminately across Permian, Paleozoic and Archaean outcrops alike. The plateaux are in fact erosional features and represent uplifted erosion surfaces or peneplanes. In a few places, mountain ranges of particularly resistant rock rise above the general level, notably the **Gory Putorana** (Putoran Mountains) which reach nearly 7000 ft (2100 m). The plateau is dissected by river systems tributary to the Yenisey and Lena, which flow northwards below its western and eastern edges respectively. These include the Vilyuy in the east and the Nizhnyaya Tunguska (Lower Tungus), Podkamennaya Tunguska (stony Tungus) and Angara in the west.

The plateau gives way northward to the **Severo-Sibirskaya Nizmennost'** (North Siberian Lowland) or Khatanga Depression, an eastward extension of the West Siberian Lowland. This in turn is bounded on its northern side by the Hercynian uplands of the **Poluostrov Taymyr** (Taymyr Peninsula).

Along the south-western edge of the plateau, the **Yeniseyskiy Kryazh** (Yenisey Ridge), Caledonian in origin, runs in a north-west to south-east direction, rising abruptly to more than 3000 ft (900 m) from the eastern bank of the Yenisey River. The Caledonian fold ranges continue south-eastward into the **Sayanskiy Khrebet** (Sayan Mountain system) whence they turn abruptly north-eastward to run along the south-eastern flank of the Anabar Shield. In this region, the mountain system has been subjected to peneplanation followed by re-elevation. The latter took the form of block faulting to give *horst* and *graben* country on a massive scale. The summits of the uplifted blocks often rise to more than 6000 ft (1800 m) and are separated from the rift valleys by extremely steep fault scarps. One of the valleys contains **Ozero Baykal** (Lake Baykal) which is practically 400 miles (640 km) long and about 30 miles (48 km) across. While the mountains on either side reach 6600 ft (2000 m), the bottom of the lake is 4250 ft (1300 m) below sea-level, a total height range of nearly 11,000 ft (3300 m). This is the world's deepest lake (maximum depth of water 5745 ft (1752 m)) and has its own unique fauna.

The Caledonian belt as a whole decreases in altitude northwards and eventu-ally passes into the **Middle Lena Basin** or **Tsentral'no-Yakutskaya Niz-mennost'** (Central Yakut Basin) where the ancient structures are concealed beneath sedimentary rocks and where the surface is largely of Jurassic materials. This basin forms a lowland stretching nearly 500 miles (900 km) in an east–west direction between the eastern edge of the Siberian plateau and the moun-tains of the Far East.

East of the Caledonian belt, between the Middle Lena Basin and the Manchu-rian frontier, is the **Aldan Shield** over most of which Archaean metamorphic and igneous materials are exposed at the surface to give mountainous country of strong relief. The highest ranges are those of the **Stanovoy Khrebet** (Stanovoy Mountains) which rise to 8200 ft (2460 m).

THE SOUTHERN AND EASTERN MOUNTAIN RANGES

The remainder of the territory of the Soviet Union is occupied by complex fold-mountain systems. These are discussed together here, since they form a continuous barrier along the southern frontier and behind the Pacific coast, but it should be realized that they vary a great deal in their date of origin, rock type and landforms. As the map of tectonic zones (Fig. 3) indicates, the Caledonian system is confined to the southern part of eastern Siberia where it forms an arc around the southern edge of the Anabar Shield. Mountains of Hercynian origin cover a good deal of Soviet Central Asia as well as the Urals. The Meso-zoic system occupies the greater part of the Far Eastern region together with a structural trough, now generally low-lying, which runs from Belorussia through the Donbass and across the Caspian into the western part of Central Asia. Mountains of Tertiary (Alpine) origin include the Carpathians, the Krymskiye Gory (Crimean range), the Kavkazskiy Khrebet (Caucasus) and the southernmost part of Central Asia. To the east of the last region they run outside Soviet territory but recur in the Sakhalin-Kamchatka area of the Far East. There are important contrasts between the Caledonian and Hercynian mountain systems on the one hand and, on the other, those formed in Mesozoic and Alpine times. The former, having been exposed to the forces of sub-aerial denudation for long periods are generally of fairly low elevation, with gentle slopes and broad, open valleys. Where steep slopes do occur, these are often the result of recent block-faulting. One valuable result of the geological history of these areas, is the exposure at or near the surface of mineral-rich metamorphic and igneous rocks. The younger mountain zones, and particularly those produced by the Alpine orogeny, have not been denuded to anything like the same degree, though they have of course been vigorously dissected by rivers and glaciers. As a result, they stand at much greater heights and have sharper landforms and steeper slopes. Since they are composed of tightly folded sedimentary rocks they rarely contain an abundance of mineral wealth. In the account which follows, attention will be concentrated on the relief and landforms of the various mountain areas rather than on their geological structure.

Karpaty (*The Carpathians*)

Since the addition to the Soviet Union after the Second World War of the former Czech province of Ruthenia (the sub-Carpathian Ukraine) a small section of the Carpathian Mountains is now included in Soviet territory.

Krymskiye Gory (*The Crimean Mountains*)

In comparison with the other great mountain systems of the U.S.S.R., these are a small mountainous belt some 20 miles (32 km) wide and 65 miles (104 km) long, backing the southern coast of the Crimean peninsula. There are three parallel ridges of which the southernmost is the highest reaching a little above 5000 ft (1500 m).

Kavkazskiy Khrebet (*The Caucasus*)

This is a much more complex system, which occupies the large isthmus between the Black Sea and the southern part of the Caspian. There are three major subdivisions: the **Bol'shoy Kavkaz** (Greater Caucasus or Main Caucasian Range), the Trans-Caucasian Depression and the **Malyy Kavkaz** (Lesser Caucasus).

Bol'shoy Kavkaz (The Greater Caucasus). A major anticlinal axis, structurally continuous with that of the Crimea, covers a distance of 700 miles (1100 km) from Novorossiysk on the Black Sea to the Apsheron peninsula on the Caspian. The western part of this anticline has been breached by erosion to expose a central core of granites and metamorphic rocks, flanked on either side by zones of folded Mesozoic materials. The crest of this core area exceeds 12,000 ft (3600 m) over a considerable distance, the highest point of all being **Gora El'brus**, Mt. Elbruz (18,470 ft; 5633 m). The eastern half of the anticline remains unbreached and Mesozoic rocks are continuous right across it. Here the main crest is somewhat lower (7000–9000 ft; 2100–2700 m) but a number of peaks rise much higher, reaching a maximum of 14,680 ft (4477 m). The Greater Caucasus are flanked on their northern side by a zone of Tertiary plateaux which reach their widest extent in the **Stavropol'skiy Vozvyshennost'** (Stavropol' Plateau) (1900–2600 ft; 570–780 m) which projects northward to separate the low-lying plains of the Kuban' and Terek rivers.

The **Trans-Caucasian Depression** itself falls into three parts. In the west is the **Kolkhida** (Rioni Lowland), a triangular plain with its base along the Black Sea and its apex about 60 miles (100 km) inland. This is separated by the granitic **Suramskiy Khrebet** (Suram Massif) from the much larger **Kura Lowland** which runs from Tbilisi to the Caspian, a distance of about 300 miles (480 km), and is 100 miles (160 km) across at its widest part.

Malyy Kavkaz (The Lesser Caucasus) is a good deal more varied in its structure than is the main range. On its northern side, numerous fold ranges, rising to 9000 or 10,000 ft (2700–3000 m) overlook the Rioni and Kura plains. To the south of these ranges is the **Armyanskoye Nagor'ye** (Armenian Plateau). Here, the original fold structures have been broken up by large-scale block faulting to give a series of plateaux and high-level basins. The picture is further complicated by the presence of vast spreads of Tertiary lavas, poured out in association with the rifting. **Ozero Sevan** (Lake Sevan) (545 sq miles; 1412 sq km) lies in a basin whose exit has been dammed by lava flows. The Lesser Caucasus fall away southward to the Araks valley which forms the Soviet frontier with Turkey and Iran.

THE MOUNTAINS OF SOVIET CENTRAL ASIA

The major fold axis represented by the Main Caucasian Range is continued to the east of the Caspian in the **Khrebet Bol'shoy Balkhan** and **Khrebet Kopet Dag** ranges. The latter, which form the northern edge of the Iranian Plateau, rise to heights of more than 9000 ft (2700 m) along the southern frontier of the Turkmen Republic.

A vast and complex system of mountain ranges, basins and plateaux occupies the south-eastern part of Soviet Central Asia. The major elements are listed below.

Gory Pamir (The Pamirs) form part of the "Pamir Knot", a focal zone in the Alpine fold system from which high ranges stretch north-eastward along the Soviet–Chinese frontier, south-eastward into Kashmir and Tibet and westward into Afghanistan. The Soviet section occupies the eastern part of the

Tadzhik Republic and contains the two highest points in the U.S.S.R.: **Pik Lenina,** Lenin Peak (23,363 ft; 7126 m) and **Pik Kommunizm,** Mt. Communism (24,590 ft; 7500 m).

The **Alay** mountain system is separated from the Pamirs by the Surkhob valley. Its ranges run westward from the Chinese frontier and form the watershed between the Syr-Dar'ya and Amu-Dar'ya river systems. The crests exceed 10,000 ft (3000 m) in the Kirgiz and Tadzhik republics but further west, in Uzbekistan, they become progressively lower, terminating in a series of disconnected hills, 2000–2500 ft (600–750 m) high, rising above the Kyzyl-Kum desert.

The **Basin of the Upper Amu-Dar'ya** forms the southern frontier of the Uzbek and Tadzhik republics. Numerous south-flowing tributaries join the main river and are separated by high mountain chains which diverge southward from the Alay range.

The **Basin of the Upper Syr-Dar'ya (Ferganskaya Dolina or Fergana Basin)** is a fault-bounded trough standing between 1000 and 1500 ft (300–450 m) above sea-level. Being virtually surrounded by abrupt mountain slopes, this is a very well-defined physiographic unit.

The **Tyan' Shan'** mountain system is represented in the Soviet Union by a belt of territory between the Syr-Dar'ya and Balkhash basins. Here, as in the Alay, a broad complex of mountain ranges, rising well above 10,000 ft (3000 m), declines towards the west. The system is prolonged north-westward into the desert by the **Kara-Tau** range. **Ozero Issyk-Kul'** (Issyk-Kul) is a high altitude moraine-drained lake.

The **Balkhash Basin,** between the Tyan' Shan' and the Kazakh Upland is a plateau, largely desert, between 1000 and 1200 ft (300–360 m) above sea-level.

The **Upper Irtysh Basin** occupies the north-eastern part of Kazakhstan and lies between the Kazakh Upland and the Altai Mountains.

From this brief description, it is readily apparent that the south-eastern part of Soviet Central Asia is an area of extreme diversity in relief. The mountains, save where they contain workable mineral deposits, are of relatively little value to mankind. The plateaux, basins and mountain-foot plains, however, with their fertile soils derived from *loess* and alluvium, are of great agricultural importance, especially where a plentiful supply of water is available.

THE MOUNTAINS OF SOUTHERN SIBERIA AND THE FAR EAST

The alignment of the main mountain ranges in these regions is indicated in Fig. 5. Detailed description of the whole of this area is impossible within the compass of this volume and we must confine ourselves to a summary of the major elements.

The **Altai** and **Sayan** ranges constitute the southern part of Siberia from the Irtysh valley to Lake Baykal. The Altai system, between the Irtysh and Yenisey

FIG. 5. Surface configuration. Most of the relief regions listed in Chapter 1 are located on this map. (Based on a map appearing on page 13 of *Economic Geography of the U.S.S.R.* by S. S. Bal'zak, V. F. Vasyutin and Y. G. Feigin. Copyright 1949 by the American Council of Learned Societies. Used with permission of the Macmillan Company.)

AFTER BAL'ZAK, VASYUTIN & FEIGIN

MOUNTAINS

HILLS & LOW PLATEAUS

PLAINS

500 MILES

500 KM

List of physical features, which appear on the face of the map in vernacular form, with their conventional English equivalents.

Vernacular	*Conventional English*
Alay, Gory	Alay Mts.
Altai, Gory	Altai Mts.
Amu-Dar'ya	Amu-Darya
Anadyr' Khrebet	Anadyr Mts.
Armyanskoye Nagor'ye	Armenian Plateau
Bol'shoy Kavkaz	Main Caucasus Range
Bureinskiy Khrebet	Bureyinsk Mts.
Cherskiy Khrebet	Chersky Mts.
Donetskiy Kryazh	Donets Mts.
Dzhugdzhur, Khrebet	Dzugdzhur Mts.
Ferganskaya Dolina	Fergana Basin
Frantsa-Iosifa, Zemlya	Franz Josef Land
Karpaty	Carpathian Mts.
Kazakhskiy Melkosopochnik	Kazakh Upland
Kolkhida	Rioni Basin
Kol'skiy Poluostrov	Kola Peninsula
Kolymskaya Nizmennost'	Kolymsk Lowland
Kolymskiy Khrebet	Kolymsk Mts.
Kopet Dag, Khrebet	Kopet Dag
Koryaksiy Khrebet	Koryak Mts.
Krymskiye Gory	Crimean Mts.
Kuril'skiye Ostrova	Kuril Islands
Malyy Kavkaz	Lesser Caucasus
Novosibirskiye Ostrova	New Siberian Islands
Pamir, Gory	Pamir Mts.
Peski Kara-Kum	Kara Kum Desert
Peski Kyzyl-Kum	Kyzyl Kum Desert
Peski Muyun-Kum	Muyun Kum Desert
Poles'ye	Polesye
Pribaykal'ye	Pre-Baykalia
Privolzhskaya Vozvyshennost'	Pre-Volga Heights
Putorana, Gory	Putoran Mts.
Sayanskiy Khrebet	Sayan Mts.
Severnaya Dvina	N. Dvina
Severo-Sibirskaya Nizmennost'	North Siberian Lowland
Sikhota-Alin'	Sikhota Alin
Smolensko-Moskovskaya Vozvyshennost'	Smolensk-Moscow Ridge
Sredne-Sibirskoye Ploskogor'ye	Central Siberian Plateau
Sredny Russkaya Vozvyshennost'	Central Russian Elevation
Stanovoy Khrebet	Stanovoy Mts.
Syr-Dar'ya	Syr-Darya
Taymyr, Poluostrov	Taymyr Peninsula
Timanskiy Kryazh	Timan Mts.
Tsentral'no-Yakutskaya Nizmennost'	Turgay Gate
Turanskaya Nizmennost'	Middle Lena Basin
Turgayskiye Vorota	Turanian Lowland
Tyan' Shan'	Tyan Shan Mts.
Ural, Severnyy	Northern Urals
Ural, Sredniy	Central Urals
Ural, Yuzhnyy	Southern Urals
Ustyurt, Plato	Ust Urt Plateau
Valdayskaya Vozvyshennost'	Valday Hills
Verkhoyanskiy Khrebet	Verkhoyansk Mts.
Volyno-Podol'skaya Vozvyshennost'	Volyno-Podolsk Upland
Yablonovyy Khrebet	Yablonovy Mts.
Yeniseyskiy Kryazh	Yenisey Mts.
Zabaykal'ye	Trans Baykalia
Zapadnaya Dvina	W. Dvina
Zapadno-Sibirskaya Nizmennost'	North Siberian Lowland

rivers, rises in places to more than 15,000 ft (4500 m) and its northward-projecting ridges enclose the **Kuznetsk** and **Minusinsk** basins. Beyond the Yenisey, the Sayan ranges form a barrier between Siberia proper and the Tuvinian Autonomous Republic.

Pribaykal'ye and Zabaykal'ye (Pre- and Trans-Baykalia) is a region of block-faulted mountain ranges and basins whose general features have already been commented upon. The major range in this region is the **Yablonovyy Khrebet** (Yablonovy), which forms a water divide between the Arctic and Pacific drainage basins.

Beyond the Yablonovy Mountains, two mountain systems diverge. One runs north-eastward around the eastern edge of the Siberian platform and fans out to occupy the whole area between the Lena and the Pacific Ocean. A second system occupies the southern part of the Far Eastern region between the Pacific and the Manchurian frontier.

The Far North-East. The Lena Basin is separated from areas draining into the Sea of Okhotsk by the **Stanovoy** and **Dzhugdzhur** ranges. The latter is continued northward by the **Verkhoyanskiy** Mountains which reach the Arctic Ocean close to the Lena Delta. To the east of this system, the **Cherskiy** and **Kolymskiy** (Gydan) ranges enclose the northward-facing **Kolymskaya Nizmennost'** (Kolyma Basin). The **Chukotskiy (Anadyr')** Mountains are a separate system occupying the most remote north-eastern part of the Soviet Union, while the **Koryakskiy** (Koryak) and **Kamchatskiy (Sredinnyy)** ranges are part of an axis of folding which is continued southward through the Kurile Islands into Japan.

The Far South-East. A somewhat confused mountain zone in which the **Tukuringra** and **Bureinskiy** ranges are the most important, occurs between the Stanovoy ranges and the River Amur. Between the **Amur–Ussuri Lowland** and the Sea of Japan are the **Sikhota-Alin'** which reach a maximum height of nearly 10,000 ft (3000 m).

In contrast to conditions over the Soviet Union as a whole, southern Siberia and the Far East are regions in which mountain territory predominates. The largest lowlands are in high latitudes of extremely harsh climate and extensive lowlands in more temperate latitudes are confined to the valleys of the Amur–Ussuri drainage system.

In conclusion, attention may be drawn to the simple map of surface configuration (Fig. 5) which divides the Soviet Union into areas of plain, hill or plateau and mountain. The major features of the country's relief are immediately apparent. True mountain territory is confined to the southern and eastern parts, the only exception being that provided by the Urals, while plains are virtually continuous over the European and West Siberian sections and over much of Soviet Central Asia.

CHAPTER 2

CLIMATE, SOILS, VEGETATION

CLIMATE

In all regional studies of climate, three major factors must be taken into account. These are latitude, altitude and distance from the sea.

Latitude

The Soviet Union stretches through a wide latitudinal range. Discounting the islands in the Arctic Ocean, Soviet territory extends from latitude 78°N. (Taymyr peninsula) to 36° N. (southern Turkmeniya). However, since the country widens northwards and has its greatest longitudinal extent close to the Arctic Circle, the bulk of the U.S.S.R. is situated in high latitudes. Three-quarters of the country is north of the 50th parallel and when we recall that the whole of the U.S.A. (with the exception of Alaska) is south of latitude 49°N., we can see that the U.S.S.R. is at a great disadvantage in this respect.

LATITUDINAL DISTRIBUTION OF THE
LAND AREA OF THE U.S.S.R.

	%
North of 70°N.	5·2
60 – 70°N.	34·3
50 – 60°N.	40·9
40 – 50°N.	16·8
South of 40°N.	2·8

Altitude

As the previous chapter has shown, the Soviet Union is predominantly a low-lying country, some three-quarters of which is less than 1500 ft (450 m) above sea-level. As a result, districts in which the local climate is fundamentally affected by altitude are relatively restricted in extent. Mountainous zones are confined to southern and eastern parts of the country where they form strong barriers between the U.S.S.R. and the outside world. In contrast, the interior is open northward to the Arctic Ocean and westward towards the Atlantic

17

without the intervention of any major relief feature. This arrangement is extremely important in the effect it has on climatic conditions.

Distance from the Sea

The vast size of the Soviet Union ensures that some 75 per cent of its territory is more than 250 miles (400 km) from the sea, this distance reaching a maximum of more than 1500 miles (2400 km) in parts of southern Siberia. The longest coastline is that of the Arctic Ocean, frozen for more than half the year, while the Pacific shore is washed by cold currents and separated from the interior by high mountain ranges. As a result, maritime influences from these two water bodies are of limited importance and it is the Atlantic which has most effect, its influence being discernible to a slight degree, as far east as the Yenisey.

The combination of these three factors—high latitude, low altitude and great distance from the sea—means that the greater part of the Soviet Union has a continental climatic régime characterized by great extremes of temperature and relatively small amounts of rainfall. Only in a few peripheral areas such as the Crimean coast, Transcaucasia, parts of Central Asia and the Far East are other varieties of climate to be found.

Pressure and Winds (Fig. 6)

In the winter months, rapid cooling of the Asiatic land mass results in the development of an intense high-pressure system in the heart of the continent. This is generally centred in the vicinity of Lake Baykal where barometric pressure remains around 30·6 in. (1020 mb) for long periods. A ridge of high pressure extends westward, roughly along latitude 50°N. and from this ridge there is a marked pressure gradient north-westward towards the Icelandic low pressure system. The ridge acts as a wind divide, winds to the north of the ridge being predominantly from the west while those to the south of the ridge come mainly from the east. Since westerly winds are, relatively speaking, mild and those from the east are cold, the temperature differences which one would expect to occur with latitude are much reduced. To the east of the Siberian high pressure there is a pressure gradient towards the low pressure system developed in the area of the Aleutian Islands and winds blow from the north or north-west throughout the Soviet Far East. As a result, the ameliorating effect of the Pacific Ocean, which is in any case reduced by the presence of cold currents offshore, is confined to a narrow coastal strip.

In the summer months, pressure conditions are completely reversed. The Siberian high is replaced by a low pressure system which is centred over Baluchistan, but extends north-eastward to the shores of the Arctic Ocean. Within the Soviet Union, the depression is shallow (min. 29·6 in. or 1002 mb) and pressure gradients are gentle. A weak ridge of high pressure extends eastward into the country along latitude 50°N. and this has some effect on wind direction. Over the European plain and western Siberia, winds are from the west and north-west, in Central Asia they blow from the north and north-east. Along the shores of the Arctic, they are mainly from the east. In the Far East, the prevailing winds are those of the south-easterly summer monsoon which affects the whole of the Pacific shore of Asia.

Fig. 6. Pressure conditions and prevailing winds in (A) January and (B) July. Isobars at 2 mb intervals.

Temperature (Fig. 7)

In the winter, the influence of the Atlantic, carried by the prevailing wester-lies, extends to the Yenisey and isotherms run from north-west to south-east over the European plain and the West Siberian Lowland, showing that in these regions the oceanic influence is more important than that of latitude, despite the big differences in insolation from north to south. The temperature of the coldest month at Arkhangel'sk (lat. 65°N.) is within one degree of that at Kazan' (lat. 55°N.). Conversely, there is a rapid falling-off of temperatures eastward along any given latitude, the lowest monthly means being 27°F (—3°C) at Kaliningrad, 14°F (—10°C) at Moscow, 7°F (—14°C) at Kazan' and —3°F (—20°C) at Tomsk in south-west Siberia. This gradation is continued eastward to beyond the Lena where Verkhoyansk (Jan. mean —58°F, —50°C) claims the distinction of the lowest temperature ever recorded outside the Antarctic, namely —90°F (—50°C) or 122 degrees of frost. Beyond this zone of extremely low temperatures, the isotherms again curve round to run from north to south, reflecting the slight warming effect of the Pacific. Even here, however, the

FIG. 7. Temperature conditions in (A) January and (B) July.

term "warm" is wholly relative. Petropavlovsk-Kamchatskiy (Petropavlovsk in Kamchatka) registers a January mean of 17°F (—8°C), Okhotsk —13°F (—25°C) and even Vladivostok, which is in the same latitude as Florence, has a January mean of only 6°F (—9°C). In fact there are very few areas in the U.S.S.R. where the coldest month has a mean above freezing point. These include the Crimean coast (Yalta 39°F, 4°C) and Transcaucasia (Batumi 43°F, 6°C). Most of Soviet Central Asia has low winter temperatures (Turtkul' 23°F, —5°C). There is a small area along the southern margin with no monthly mean below 32°F (0°C) but even here frosts are a common occurrence.

In summer the effect of latitude on temperature does make itself felt and isotherms run in an east–west direction across most of the country. However, the moderating influence of the sea is apparent in the eastern and western extremities. In the Baltic region and over the European plain generally, isotherms trend towards the south-west, while in the Far East they turn abruptly southward, indicating the lowering of temperatures associated with the strong onshore winds of the summer monsoon. The lowest summer temperatures are recorded along the Arctic shores, where the 50°F (10°C) July isotherm runs parallel to the coast (Sagastyr 41°F, 5°C; Malyye Karmakuly 44°F, 7°C). The highest July means are found in Soviet Central Asia where values exceed 75°F (24°C) over large areas (Tashkent 80°F, 27°C; Turtkul' 82°F, 28°C). In the west the moderating influence of the Atlantic is reflected in the figures for Leningrad and Kaliningrad (both 63°F, 17°C). On the Pacific coast, Vladivostok has an August mean of 69°F (20°C), but further north the summer is little warmer than

FIG. 8. Average number of days in the year with mean temperatures below freezing point (black). Average duration of snow cover in days (red).

it is along the shores of the Arctic (Petropavlovsk 52°F, 11°C; Okhotsk 53°F, 12°C). Summer temperatures vary much less from one part of the country to another than do those of winter. The highest and lowest July means are those of Tashkent (80°F, 27°C) and Sagastyr (41°F, 5°C), a difference of 39°F (22°C) whereas in January the range is from 43°F (6°C) at Batumi to −58°F (−50°C) at Verkhoyansk, a difference of 101°F (56°C).

A characteristic of continental climates which is well illustrated in the U.S.S.R. is the large temperature range between the hottest and coldest months. Since winter temperatures vary more than those of summer, it follows that variations in the temperature range are largely a product of differences in the winter means. Thus the temperature range is at its maximum in the interior of eastern Siberia where Verkhoyansk has a range between the hottest and coldest months of 117°F (65°C), the largest in the world. Even in coastal areas, however, the range is generally large, more than 30°F (17°C) along the Baltic and over 60°F (34°C) along the Pacific coast. Further details of temperature conditions at various stations will be found later in this chapter.

As an indication of the predominance of cold climates in the Soviet Union, mention should be made of the average duration of the frost-free period (Fig. 8). In the extreme north an average year has fewer than seventy days with a mean temperature above freezing point, the number rising to about 180 along the southern boundary of Siberia. In the European part of the country, the range is from about 170 days along the north coast to 300 on the Black Sea and a maximum of 340 in the southern Crimea. In Soviet Central Asia there is a north–south increase from about 200 in central Kazakhstan to 340 along the southern frontier.

Precipitation (Fig. 9)

The low relief and continental character of the U.S.S.R. ensure that precipitation over most of the country is moderate or light. The greater part of the inhabited area receives between 16 and 20 in. (400–500 mm) annually, figures typical of much of the European plain and West Siberian Lowland. Areas receiving larger amounts do so for a variety of reasons. The north-western part of the European plain (Riga 24 in., 600 mm) shows the effect of the Atlantic maritime influence brought by the prevailing westerly winds which are also responsible for totals above 20 in. recorded along the western flank of the Urals. The higher parts of the mountains of Soviet Central Asia and south-west Siberia illustrate the effect of altitude on precipitation, amounts ranging from 16 in. (400 mm) in the foothills to 50 in. (1250 mm) or more on the higher peaks. In the Far East, the summer monsoon is responsible for heavy rain on the Sikhota-Alin' and in the Kamchatka peninsula. The highest totals of all are recorded on the south-western flank of the Caucasus where a combination of

AVERAGE ANNUAL RAINFALL

OVER 1000MM (40 INCHES APPROX)
600-1000 MM (24-40 INCHES APPROX)
400-600 MM (16-24 " ")
200-400 MM (8-16 " ")
100-200 MM (4-8 " ")
LESS THAN 100MM (4 " ")

MILES
0   500
KILOMETRES
0   500

FIG. 9. **Average annual precipitation.** Note the comparatively small areas which
receive more than 600 mm (c. 24 in.) per annum.

moist winds from the Black Sea and steep relief give 93 in. (2325 mm) at Batumi.

There are large areas receiving less than 16 in. (400 mm) and these occur in two zones. The first comprises eastern Siberia and the interior lowlands of the Far East. Here there is a decline in precipitation northward towards the Arctic Ocean; lowlands from the Lena eastwards receive less than 8 in. (200 mm), Sagastyr recording 3·3 in. (82·5 mm). In the second area, Soviet Central Asia, there is a progressive diminution towards desert conditions in the centre of the region ('Turtkul' 2·4 in., 60 mm).

Throughout most of the Soviet Union, precipitation shows the marked summer maximum associated with the continental climate or, along the Pacific coast, with the onshore monsoon. The most important exception to this general rule is provided by the area along the eastern Black Sea coast from the Crimea to the Turkish frontier, where the predominance of winter depressions passing through the Black Sea gives a winter rainfall maximum. This is also the case in the interior of Central Asia, though here amounts in all seasons are, of course, small.

NATURAL REGIONS

The close inter-relationships between climate, soils and vegetation make it imperative that these three elements in the physical environment should be considered together in any discussion of natural regions. The effect of climate on vegetation is fairly obvious. Any plant or group of plants can only grow within a certain, often quite limited range of climatic conditions, the most important elements in this respect being temperature, precipitation, humidity and wind. Thus the major vegetation belts are closely allied to the major climatic zones. Similarly, plants have certain requirements in the form of moisture and both inorganic and organic chemical compounds which they can only obtain from the soil so that the relationship between vegetation and soil type is equally close. Plants in turn affect the soil in which they grow particularly in so far as its organic content is concerned. That the major soil types (Fig. 10) are themselves largely a product of climate is, perhaps, a rather less familiar idea which may require some elaboration. It is particularly fitting that this concept should be discussed here since it was originally formulated by Russian soil scientists notably by Dokuchayev. Dokuchayev and his contemporaries, working in the great European plain of Russia in the late nineteenth century, clearly demonstrated that the major soil belts are arranged in roughly parallel zones, running from east to west across the country and are closely related to the major climatic zones. Soil is, in fact, the end product of the weathering processes and, since the character of these processes depends largely on climate, it is not surprising that soil and climate should be closely related. Precipitation and evaporation, by affecting the movement of soluble chemical compounds within the soil, have a

SOILS

Fig. 10. Soils. Only the major (zonal) soil types are distinguished.

TUNDRA SOILS

PODSOLS

GREY & BROWN FOREST EARTHS

BLACK EARTHS

CHESTNUT SOILS

DESERT SOILS

RED AND YELLOW EARTHS

MOUNTAIN MEADOW AND STEPPE SOILS

MILES 0 1000

KILOMETRES 0 1000

profound effect on the chemical composition of the various soil layers or *horizons* which make up the veritcal section or *profile* of the soil. Under a given set of climatic conditions, a major soil type (*zonal* soil) will develop, regardless of the parent material from which that soil is derived. Conversely, a particular rock type will break down into a variety of zonal soils in different areas according to the climatic conditions prevailing within each area. Within each major soil region, however, special local conditions of parent material and drainage may exert a strong-enough influence to create a local soil type (e.g. a marsh soil) which differs appreciably from the zonal type. Such soils are said to be *intrazonal*. In areas where the fully mature soil profile associated with a particular climate has not yet developed (e.g. in areas of recent glacial deposition or of continuing alluvial deposition) an *azonal* soil type may be found. This too differs considerably from the mature, zonal soil. Thus the correspondence between climate, soil and vegetation belts is by no means exact in every respect. As a result, it is often expedient to choose one element only for the delineation of natural regions and, since it is the element most easily recognized on the ground, the choice frequently falls on vegetation. If vegetation regions are defined (Fig. 11), one can confidently expect them to reflect local conditions of soil and climate. This is the procedure adopted in this book where the following natural regions will be discussed in turn.

1. Tundra
2. Coniferous Forest
3. Mixed and Deciduous Forest
4. Wooded Steppe
5. Steppe
6. Dry Steppe and Semi-Desert
7. Desert
8. Humid Sub-Tropics
9. Southern Mountain Areas

1. Tundra

The Tundra region, which occupies about 15 per cent of the area of the U.S.S.R., lies to the north of the 50°F (10°C) July isotherm so that summers are cool as well as being short. Winters are cold, though less so than further inland, and become increasingly severe towards the east. Precipitation is light, ranging from about 15 in. (375 mm) along the shores of the Barents Sea to less than 4 in. (100 mm) near the Lena delta. The greater part falls as summer drizzle. Snow may occur at almost any time of the year, but snow cover is limited in extent and depth partly because of the limited precipitation and partly because of the strong winds which often sweep the surface clear. Atmospheric humidity is high, the sky is clouded over for at least 75 per cent of the time and coastal fogs are common.

VEGETATION

TUNDRA

CONIFEROUS FOREST

MIXED & DECIDUOUS FOREST

BIRCH - ASPEN FOREST

USSURI DECIDUOUS FOREST ZONE

CAUCASIAN DECIDUOUS FOREST ZONE

WOODED STEPPE

STEPPE

SEMI-DESERT

DESERT

MOUNTAIN GRASSLAND

SUB-TROPICAL FOREST

MILES   1000

0   KILOMETRES   1000

FIG. 11. Vegetation. This map forms the basis on which natural regions are discussed in Chapter 2.

SAGASTYR (125°E., 73°N., 11 ft (3 m) a.s.l.)*

	J	F	M	A	M	J	J	A	S	O	N	D	Yr
Temp. °F	—34	—36	—30	—7	5	32	41	38	33	6	—16	—32	
°C	—37	—38	—35	—22	—15	0	5	3	1	—14	—27	—35	
Pptn. in.	0·1	0·1	0·0	0·0	0·2	0·4	0·3	1·4	0·4	0·1	0·1	0·2	3·3
mm	2·5	2·5	0·0	0·0	5·1	10·2	7·6	35·6	10·2	2·5	2·5	5·1	83·8

* The position of climatic stations used as examples is shown in Fig. 12.

In all but the extreme western part of the Tundra region, the subsoil is permanently frozen, the top few feet thawing out in the summer months (permafrost layer: see below). As a result, drainage is extremely poor, particularly in flat, low-lying areas. Under these conditions, the decay of organic matter is slow and soils are highly acid. Where steeper slopes occur and drainage is better, leached podsols (see below) are found, but these are quite rare. Conditions are highly unfavourable to plant growth and the natural vegetation is very restricted in its range. In the northernmost area (*arctic tundra*) it is confined to lichen and mosses. Further south, in the *shrubby tundra*, stunted willow and birch occur together with bilberry and some grasses, but lichens and mosses remain widespread. The shrubby tundra gives way southward through a transitional zone where trees occur along river courses to the *wooded tundra*, in which forest is common on interfluves as well as in valleys and sphagnum peat bogs become extremely widespread.

FIG. 12. Location of towns for which climatic data are given in Chapter 2.

Permafrost is ground in which the moisture below the surface is permanently frozen and the permafrost zone covers no less than 3,860,000 sq miles (9,997,400 sq km), some 45 per cent of the territory of the U.S.S.R. The thickness of the permafrost layer varies from about 3 ft (1 m) along the southern boundary to more than 1200 ft (360 m) along the shores of the Arctic Ocean. The permanently

EXTENT OF PERMAFROST

⊞ ZONE OF CONTINUOUS PERMAFROST
▥ ZONE OF DISCONTINUOUS PERMAFROST

FIG. 13. The extent of permafrost conditions.

frozen subsoil is covered by a layer which freezes in winter and thaws in summer, the depth to which it thaws depending on local conditions of climate, vegetation, relief and drainage. Permafrost is not continuous throughout the zone (Fig. 13) which falls into a number of subdivisions. These include islands of permafrost in thawing ground and islands of permafrost outside the main mass, some of them in the high mountain areas of the south. Thick seams of fossil ice 30–40 ft (10–12 m) below the surface of the ground, together with the preserved bodies of mammoth and hairy rhinoceros in the permafrost indicate that it is a relic of the Pleistocene ice-age and has been continuously in existence since that period. The total area of permafrost is now declining as the southern boundary retreats slowly northward, but the climate in the north of the zone is such as to ensure its persistence there for a long time to come. Permafrost is a major obstacle to the development of much of Siberia. Mining, transport development and any form of building works have to adopt special techniques which add appreciably to the cost of construction.

It should be noted that tundra conditions of climate, soil and vegetation occur on many high mountain areas of Siberia outside the main tundra zone.

2. Coniferous Forest (Taiga)

This is by far the largest and most continuous of the natural regions, occupying the European and West Siberian Lowlands north of latitudes 56–58°N. as well as the greater part of the U.S.S.R. east of the Yenisey. Over such a vast area there are considerable differences of climate, soil and vegetation, but the region has a basic unity derived from its extreme continentality, its podsolic soils and the predominance of coniferous forest. The taiga is usually divided into western and eastern sections along the line of the River Yenisey, reflecting the fact that temperature conditions become more extreme and rainfall diminishes from west to east.

In the *western taiga*, cyclonic influences from the Atlantic make themselves felt throughout the year. The total precipitation exceeds 20 in. (500 mm) over much of the European section and is between 16 and 20 in. (400–500 mm) in the West Siberian Lowland. More than 30 per cent falls as snow in the winter months. Summers are warm, with July means between 50° and 65°F (10–18°C); winters are long and cold, January means ranging from 18°F (−8°C) at Leningrad to −17°F (−27°C) along the middle Lena.

LENINGRAD (60°N., 30°E., 30 ft (9 m) a.s.l.)

	J	F	M	A	M	J	J	A	S	O	N	D	Yr
Temp. °F	18	18	25	37	49	58	63	60	51	41	30	22	
°C	−8	−8	−4	3	9	14	17	15	11	5	−1	−6	
Pptn. in.	0·9	0·8	0·9	0·9	1·7	1·8	2·7	2·7	2·0	1·7	1·4	1·2	18·7
mm	22·9	20·3	22·9	22·9	43·2	45·7	68·6	68·6	50·8	43·2	35·6	30·5	475·2

TURUKHANSK (66°N., 88°E., 150 ft (46 m) a.s.l.)

	J	F	M	A	M	J	J	A	S	O	N	D	Yr
Temp. °F	−17	−3	3	18	33	50	59	54	24	23	−2	−13	
°C	−27	−20	−16	−8	1	10	15	12	−4	−5	−19	−25	
Pptn. in.	0·9	0·6	0·6	1·0	1·1	2·3	1·9	2·7	2·4	1·8	1·2	0·9	17·4
mm	22·9	15·2	15·2	25·0	27·9	58·4	48·3	68·6	61·0	45·7	30·5	22·9	442·0

The *eastern taiga* comes under the influence of the intense Siberian high-pressure system from October to April so that the winter is characterized by clear skies, light snowfall and intense cold. Throughout the region, January means are well below zero (Fahrenheit) falling below —50°F (—45°C) in Yakutia. Summers are hot, with July means above 65°F (18°C) over large areas. Annual precipitation is small: less than 16 in. (400 mm) in all parts of the region and as little as 4 in. (100 mm) in places.

VERKHOYANSK (68°N., 133°E., 330 ft (100 m) a.s.l.)

	J	F	M	A	M	J	J	A	S	O	N	D	Yr
Temp. °F	—58	—48	—22	8	35	54	59	51	36	6	—34	—52	
°C	—50	—45	—30	—13	2	12	15	11	2	—14	—37	—47	
Pptn. in.	0·2	0·1	0·0	0·1	0·2	0·5	1·2	0·9	0·2	0·2	0·2	0·2	4·0
mm	5·1	2·5	0·0	2·5	5·1	12·7	30·5	22·9	5·1	5·1	5·1	5·1	101·7

YAKUTSK (62°N., 130°E., 330 ft (100 m) a.s.l.)

	J	F	M	A	M	J	J	A	S	O	N	D	Yr
Temp. °F	—46	—35	—10	16	41	59	66	60	42	16	—21	—41	
°C	—43	—37	—23	—9	5	15	19	15	6	—9	—30	—40	
Pptn. in.	0·9	0·2	0·4	0·6	1·1	2·1	1·7	2·6	1·2	1·4	0·6	0·9	13·7
mm	22·9	5·1	10·2	15·2	27·9	53·3	43·2	66·0	30·5	35·6	15·2	22·9	348·0

The soils characteristic of the taiga zone are the *podsols* which, together with the modified podsols of the mixed and deciduous forest zone to the south, cover rather more than 50 per cent of the U.S.S.R. These soils are formed under a climate in which, over the year as a whole, precipitation exceeds evaporation and the movement of soil moisture is predominantly downward through the soil profile. The coniferous trees give rise to a highly acid raw humus layer at the surface, which decomposes slowly, producing soluble humic acids. These percolate through the soil, dissolving the iron and calcium minerals which are "leached out" of the upper horizon. The latter becomes pale in colour and highly acid. Soluble materials are redeposited at lower levels where an iron-rich hardpan often forms, impeding drainage in the upper horizons. In areas of low relief, particularly where the soil is heavy and impermeable, decomposition of organic matter and the process of leaching are hindered so that highly organic bog peat soils develop. This is particularly the case in the northern parts of the European and West Siberian Lowlands. East of the Yenisey, where the land is higher and precipitation less heavy, these conditions are generally limited to river valleys.

The character of taiga vegetation varies appreciably from one part of the zone to another. In the European section, spruce and pine are dominant but birch is also widespread. In the West Siberian Lowland, pine and larch are the main species over large areas but birch again occurs widely, particularly in the Yenisey valley, and rises to dominance along the southern fringe, where it forms an intermediate belt between the taiga and the wooded steppe (see below). Beyond the Yenisey, throughout both mountain and lowland areas, the larch is by far the most important species. Spruce is the main secondary species and is particularly widespread on the southern part of the Central Siberian Plateau.

Although the taiga contains some of the world's largest areas of continuous forest it is by no means completely tree-covered. Large stretches of bog vegetation occur in badly drained lowland areas while, on the higher mountains, coniferous forest gives way to mountain tundra.

3. Mixed and Deciduous Forest

South of the taiga lies a belt of mixed forest in which deciduous trees become progressively more important, rising to dominance in the southern part of the zone. The climate of this region, which is virtually confined to the European part of the Soviet Union, is appreciably less severe than that of the taiga. Winters are still cold and there is heavy snowfall, but temperatures fluctuate a good deal so that, in the western part of the zone at least, temporary thaws sometimes occur. In summer, the mean temperature of the hottest month is everywhere below 70°F (21°C) but midday shade temperatures in the upper 90's F (35–37°C) are common. Annual rainfall totals range from nearly 25 in. (625 mm) on the Baltic coast to less than 16 in. (400 mm) at Kazan'. Moscow, which is roughly in the centre of the zone may be taken as showing fairly typical conditions.

Moscow (56°N., 38°E., 480 ft (146 m) a.s.l.)

	J	F	M	A	M	J	J	A	S	O	N	D	Yr
Temp. °F	14	17	25	39	55	61	66	62	51	40	28	19	
°C	—10	—8	—4	4	13	16	19	17	11	4	—2	—7	
Pptn. in.	1·1	0·9	1·2	1·5	1·9	2·0	2·8	2·9	2·2	1·4	1·6	1·5	21·0
mm	27·9	22·9	30·5	38·1	48·3	50·8	71·1	73·7	55·9	35·6	40·6	38·1	533·5

The soils of the zone show a transition from true podsols in the north to *grey–brown forest earths* in the south. As temperatures become higher towards the south, evaporation increases and the leaching process becomes weaker. Thus the soils are less acid than those of the taiga and, because plant growth is more luxuriant, the organic content of the upper horizons is greater.

The predominant trees over the zone as a whole are oak and spruce, though a wide variety of other species also occurs including hornbeam, ash, maple, linden, birch and aspen. The zone becomes progressively narrower towards the east as winter temperatures become lower and rainfall diminishes so that the warmth- and moisture-loving deciduous trees disappear one by one. Thus the hornbeam, an indicator of particularly mild conditions, occurs only in the south-west, the oak and maple extend to the western foothills of the Urals while only the birch and aspen, which are especially resistant to winter cold, are found beyond those mountains. As already indicated, a narrow belt of birch–aspen forest separates the taiga from the wooded steppe in the West Siberian Lowland.

The mixed and deciduous forest belt west of the Urals has been extensively cleared for agriculture.

Far Eastern mixed forest. Mixed forests also occur in the Amur and Ussuri valleys and along the southern coastal lowlands of the Far East. The climate here is transitional between the monsoon of the Pacific seaboard and the continental interior type, showing heavy summer rainfall and low winter temperatures for the latitude.

VLADIVOSTOK (43°N., 132°E., 420 ft (143 m) a.s.l.)

	J	F	M	A	M	J	J	A	S	O	N	D	Yr
Temp. °F	6	14	27	40	49	57	65	69	62	49	30	14	
°C	—14	—10	—3	4	9	14	18	20	17	9	—1	—10	
Pptn. in.	0·3	0·4	0·7	1·2	2·1	2·9	3·3	4·7	4·3	1·9	1·2	0·6	23·6
mm	7·6	10·2	17·8	30·5	53·3	73·7	83·8	119·4	109·2	48·3	30·5	15·2	599·5

The vegetation is rich and varied including both deciduous and coniferous trees. Oak, birch, ash, pine, elm, linden and maple are all found in this region, the actual species being different from those of the European mixed forests. Along the river valleys there are stretches of rich grassland on black, alluvial soils.

4. Wooded Steppe

This zone, as its name suggests, is transitional between the forests to the north and the true steppe to the south. Its presence reflects the southward increase in temperatures and decline in precipitation across the European plain. The soils are usually described as *degraded chernozems* or *leached and podsolic black earths* and mark a further stage in the transition from true podsol to chernozem (see below). The leaching process is still present but is much weaker than in the forest soils to the north.

Vegetation in this zone is an alternation of deciduous woods and grassland. The tree cover gradually becomes less continuous and more open until, along the southern margins, woodland is confined to valley sides. The wooded steppe zone is continued across the West Siberian Lowland but in eastern Siberia this type of vegetation is found only in relatively small lowland basins.

5. Steppe

This covers about 15 per cent of the U.S.S.R., stretching in a continuous belt from the western frontier to the Altai Mountains. In eastern Siberia, it occurs in several lowland basins close to the southern frontier. The climate is both warmer and drier than in the forested zone to the north. Rainfall varies between 8 and 16 in. (200–400 mm) decreasing towards the east and south, and there is a pronounced summer maximum. The later part of the summer, however, is usually rather dry, with low relative humidity and rapid evaporation. Summers are hot; the July mean temperature is between 70° and 75°F (21–24°C) throughout the region. In winter there are three to five months with average temperatures below freezing point. The limited precipitation results in a thin and discontinuous snow cover so that the ground is exposed to the full effect of severe frost for a considerable period.

ODESSA (46°N., 31°E., 210 ft (64 m) a.s.l.)

	J	F	M	A	M	J	J	A	S	O	N	D	Yr
Temp. °F	26	29	37	47	60	68	73	71	62	52	40	32	
°C	−3	−2	3	8	15	20	23	22	17	11	4	0	
Pptn. in.	0·9	0·7	1·1	1·1	1·3	2·3	2·1	1·2	1·4	1·1	1·6	1·3	16·1
mm	22·9	17·8	27·9	27·9	33·0	58·4	53·3	30·5	35·6	27·9	40·6	33·0	408·8

SEMIPALATINSK (50°N., 80°E., 590 ft (180 m) a.s.l.)

	J	F	M	A	M	J	J	A	S	O	N	D	Yr
Temp. °F	3	4	14	37	58	67	71	67	56	38	21	9	
°C	−16	−15	−10	3	14	19	22	19	13	3	−6	−13	
Pptn. in.	0·5	0·2	0·4	0·4	0·8	0·9	1·1	0·4	0·6	0·6	0·6	0·8	7·3
mm	12·7	5·1	10·2	10·2	20·3	22·9	27·9	10·2	15·2	15·2	15·2	20·3	185·4

The steppelands are characterized by Black Earth (*chernozem*) soils. These take their name from their very dark-coloured upper horizon which is due to a high humus content, a direct result of the climatic conditions prevailing in the region. Winter frost and hot, dry summers* slow down the decomposition of organic matter, while the high summer evaporation rates prevent leaching so that the humus accumulates. Organic matter is derived from the rich cover of herbaceous vegetation typical of the steppe in its natural state and a humus-rich upper horizon more than two feet thick is characteristic throughout the Black Earth zone. Such soils are highly fertile but, being very friable, are liable to suffer soil erosion during the heavy downpours of convectional rain.

In European Russia there are very few areas in which the natural grassland of the steppe is preserved, vast stretches having been ploughed up during the last 200 years. The largest stretches of untouched steppe are found in south-west Siberia and northern Kazakhstan, the scene of the "virgin lands" project (see p. 77) where the cultivated area has been much extended since 1954. Pockets of steppeland also occur further east in Siberia.

6. Dry Steppe and Semi-Desert

Southward from the steppe, rainfall continues to decrease and summer temperatures become higher in the dry steppe and semi-desert zone which runs eastward from a line midway between the Black Sea and the Caspian. Rainfall nowhere exceeds 10 in. (250 mm), falling below 8 in. (200 mm) along the southern border. As a result, the vegetation cover becomes progressively poorer southward, the humus content of the soil decreases and chernozem is replaced by lighter-coloured *chestnut-brown soils*. These are often highly alkaline owing to the intense evaporation drawing salts to the surface, and in places saline soils (*solonetz* and *solonchak*) develop. These carry a few grasses and shrubs adapted to conditions of high alkalinity.

7. Desert

This extends from the northern and eastern shores of the Caspian to the foothills of the Alay and Tyan' Shan' mountains. A combination of low annual rainfall, cold but short winters and long, extremely hot summers with intense evaporation results in highly alkaline soils, and a poor, thin vegetation cover.

---

* Although summer is the season of maximum rainfall, this comes in heavy convectional downpours separated by lengthy periods of drought. Amounts of rain are in any case quite small over most of the region.

Turtkul' (41°N., 61°E., 295 ft (80 m) a.s.l.)

	J	F	M	A	M	J	J	A	S	O	N	D	Yr
Temp. °F	23	29	42	58	71	79	82	78	67	52	40	30	
°C	—5	—2	6	14	22	26	28	26	19	11	4	—1	
Pptn. in.	0·3	0·4	0·5	0·6	0·2	0·0	0·0	0·1	0·0	0·1	0·1	0·1	2·4
mm	7·6	10·2	12·7	15·2	5·1	0·0	0·0	2·5	0·0	2·5	2·5	2·5	60·8

There are several different types of desert. Sand desert, interspersed with stony areas, is the most common, as in the Muyun-Kum, Kyzyl-Kum and Kara-Kum. Grasses of various kinds, together with the saxaul "tree" make up the scanty natural vegetation. Around the shores of lakes, however, and along the courses of the few rivers which cross the desert, there are dense thickets of poplar and tamarisk. Clay deserts are the poorest of all with wide stretches virtually devoid of vegetation. These are most widespread on the Ustyurt and Bet Pak Dala plateaux and to the north of Lake Balkhash. The grey clay soils are interspersed with salt-encrusted *solonets* and *solonchak* areas.

8. Humid Sub-Tropics

Sub-tropical conditions are found in two regions: the Black Sea coast of Transcaucasia (the Kolkhida or Colchis Lowland) and the smaller Lenkoran' Lowland adjoining the Persian frontier west of the Caspian. The climate of these areas is characterized by mild winters, hot summers and heavy rainfall with a winter maximum.

Batumi (42°N., 42°E., 20 ft (6 m) a.s.l.)

	J	F	M	A	M	J	J	A	S	O	N	D	Yr
Temp. °F	43	44	47	52	60	68	73	74	68	61	54	48	
°C	6	7	8	11	15	20	23	23	20	16	12	9	
Pptn. in.	10·2	6·0	6·2	5·0	2·8	5·9	6·0	8·2	11·9	8·8	12·2	10·0	93·3
mm	259·1	152·4	157·4	127·0	71·1	149·9	152·4	208·3	302·3	223·5	309·9	254·0	2367·3

Soils are the *red and yellow earths* typical of the moist sub-tropics and the dominant vegetation is broad-leafed forest of oak, hornbeam, beech and poplar. In the Kolkhida Lowland, there is a dense undergrowth of evergreen bushes including holly, laurel and rhododendron as well as giant ferns, lianas and bamboo. Though small in area, these districts are of considerable agricultural importance, permitting the cultivation of crops which can be grown nowhere else in the country.

9. Southern Mountain Areas

With the exception of the humid sub-tropics, the natural regions so far described form vast belts of territory sweeping virtually without interruption across the plains and low plateaux which make up so much of the surface of the U.S.S.R. Along the southern borders of the country, however, a number of high mountain areas, by reason of their great altitudinal range, introduce more diversity, giving rise to numerous relatively small natural regions in close proximity to each other.

The smallest mountain area, that of the *southern Crimea*, can be dismissed quite briefly. The south coast of the peninsula has the nearest approach to a Mediterranean type of climate found in the Soviet Union though the marked summer drought typical of that climate is not present.

YALTA (44°N., 34°E., 135 ft (41 m) a.s.l.)

	J	F	M	A	M	J	J	A	S	O	N	D	Yr
Temp. °F	39	39	43	51	61	69	75	75	66	58	48	43	
°C	4	4	6	11	16	20	24	24	19	14	9	6	
Pptn. in.	1·8	1·6	1·6	1·3	1·1	1·5	1·3	0·9	1·4	1·7	2·0	3·0	19·2
mm	45·7	40·6	40·6	33·0	27·9	38·1	33·0	22·9	35·6	43·2	50·8	76·2	487·6

The natural vegetation to a height of about 1000 ft (300 m) above sea-level is of the Mediterranean forest type, with cypress, laurel, cork oak and Italian pine and shrubs such as myrtle, oleander and acacia. Above this is a belt of juniper-oak forest which in turn gives way to Crimean pine and then to beech. On the summit plateau there is mountain meadow grassland.

The Caucasus is a particularly complex region and nowhere else in the Soviet Union is there so great a diversity of physical conditions within such a relatively small area. This variety is a result partly of the position of the region between the Black and Caspian Seas and partly of the great range of altitude. There is a marked contrast between the western and eastern parts. The former is strongly influenced by the Black Sea, which produces, on the lower slopes at least, warm, moist conditions (see Batumi above). The Caspian, on the other hand, has little or no moderating effect on climate and the eastern Caucasus has dry climates

A Geography of the Soviet Union

with a large temperature range, conditions approaching those found in Soviet Central Asia.

TBILISI (42°N., 45°E., 1350 ft (412 m) a.s.l.)

	J	F	M	A	M	J	J	A	S	O	N	D	Yr
Temp. °F	32	37	44	53	62	70	76	76	67	57	45	37	
°C	0	3	7	12	17	21	24	24	19	14	7	3	
Pptn. in.	0·6	0·8	1·1	2·1	2·9	2·7	2·1	1·6	2·0	1·3	1·1	0·8	19·1
mm	15·2	20·3	27·9	53·3	73·7	68·6	53·3	40·6	50·8	33·0	27·9	20·3	484·9

BAKU (40°N., 50°E., 0 ft (0 m) a.s.l.)

	J	F	M	A	M	J	J	A	S	O	N	D	Yr
Temp. °F	38	39	43	51	63	72	77	77	71	62	51	44	
°C	3	4	6	11	17	22	25	25	22	17	11	7	
Pptn. in.	1·3	0·9	0·8	0·8	0·6	0·3	0·2	0·2	0·8	1·2	1·2	1·2	9·5
mm	33·0	22·9	20·3	20·3	15·2	7·6	5·1	5·1	20·3	30·5	30·5	30·5	241·3

In addition to contrasts between east and west, there is a strongly marked vertical zoning of natural conditions. Considerations of space prevent a full description of the many natural regions of the Caucasus but the description which follows gives the general picture.

The northern slope of the main Caucasian range shows clearly the effects of both altitude and the west–east diminution of rainfall. In the west, the steppe of the Don–Kuban lowlands gives way southward to a wooded steppe zone, which reaches its maximum extent on the Stavropol' Plateau. Above this is a belt of deciduous forest, which eventually grades upwards into the coniferous forest, alpine meadow and bare rock of the high mountains. In the east, in Dagestan, where conditions are much drier, the lowlands to the north of the main range are semi-desert. In the foothills, there is a belt of grassland with xerophytic shrubs which gives way to a narrow zone of deciduous forest.

Humid western Transcaucasia includes the sub-tropical Kolkhida Lowland (see above p. 36). This is succeeded inland by the deciduous forest zone. North-westward, along the Black Sea coast, conditions become progressively drier and the vegetation on the lower slopes takes on the general character of the xerophytic Mediterranean forest. At intermediate levels between the latter and the coni-

ferous forest of the higher areas is a zone of deciduous forest in which the beech
is predominant.

Dry eastern Transcaucasia is roughly coincident with the basin of the Kura
River. Beech forest occurs at intermediate levels on the north side of the basin
and below these conditions become progressively drier towards the east, giving
a gradation from steppe through semi-desert to desert along the Caspian shore.

The Armenian Plateau is largely under mountain grassland, though some of
the heights rising above the general level are covered with coniferous forest.
Southward, diminishing precipitation brings a transition to dry steppe and
semi-desert in the Yerevan basin.

Mountains of Soviet Central Asia. Here again, vertical zoning is an obvious
feature, precipitation increasing with altitude above the desert, while at the same
time conditions at any particular height become progressively drier towards the
east. Thus, basins within the mountain ranges, particularly those in the eastern
part of the region, are very dry. Forest is not at all widespread, generally occurring at intermediate levels between the desert and dry steppe of the lowlands and
foothills and the mountain grasslands of higher altitudes. It is the latter which
form the most common vegetation type of the region. They include mountain
meadows with a luxuriant grass cover in the better-watered districts and mountain steppe and semi-desert in the drier parts. Above the grasslands are zones of
alpine flora, bare rock and perpetual snow.

The Altai Mountains show a basically similar arrangement. The steppeland of
south-west Siberia rises, in the foothills, to heights of 1200 to 2000 ft (350–600
m) and is interspersed, in the higher parts of this zone, with coniferous forests of
pine, fir, spruce and larch. Above this, mountain meadows rise to about 9000 ft
(2700 m) where they give way to mountain tundra.

Mountains of Siberia and the Far East. Over most of Siberia, the mountain
slopes are covered with coniferous forest (see p. 30) and require no further
description. In the Stanovoy and Sikhota-Alin' ranges of the Far East, however,
deciduous forest extends to 1500 ft (460 m) above sea-level, while in Kamchatka
birch forest is widespread below 2000 ft (600 m).

CHAPTER 3

HISTORICAL GEOGRAPHY—
THE GROWTH OF THE RUSSIAN STATE

THE ESTABLISHMENT OF THE RUSSIAN STATE

The Soviet Union as it exists today covers a vast area of territory and includes within its boundaries a great variety of natural conditions. Having examined the physical geography of this enormous country, we must now turn our attention to its historical geography, tracing the stages by which so large an area has been brought within the frontiers of a single political unit.

Archaeological evidence points to the widespread occurrence of prehistoric settlement in what is now the southern part of European Russia but we must begin our story at the point where the Slav people first appeared on the historical scene as a distinct and recognizable group, an event which took place in the middle Danube area a century or more before the birth of Christ. Early in the second century A.D., the Slavs suffered a serious defeat at the hands of the Romans and migrated north-eastward through the Carpathians to establish themselves along the northern flank of those mountains. By the sixth century, they were in control of an area between the Vistula and Dnestr rivers which included the greater part of the Galician Plateau. From this early homeland, the Slavs spread out in several directions becoming divided, in the process, into three major groups. The west Slavs, represented today by the Poles, Slovaks and Czechs, at one time penetrated central Europe as far as the Elbe but were later driven eastward by the Teutonic peoples. A south Slav group developed in the Balkans, now the home of the Serbs, Croats and Slovenes, while the east Slavs advanced into the area which we now refer to as European Russia. It is this last group with which we are chiefly concerned.

By the ninth century A.D., the eastern Slavs had colonized much of the East European Plain, their zone of occupation extending as far north as Lake Ladoga and eastward to the upper reaches of the Volga. In extending their settlement over this area, the Slavs submerged the indigenous peoples, most of them Finno-Ugrian in origin (see below, p. 54) though traces of the latter remain in the make-up of the present-day population of the area. The southern limits of Slav settlement were roughly coincident with the boundary between forest and steppe. The steppelands at this time formed a zone of instability occupied by predominantly nomadic pastoral peoples who, on a number of occasions, burst out from their homeland in the interior of Asia and swept westward across the steppe into central Europe. The relationship of these pastoral peoples to their Slav neighbours varied. At times, the latter were left in peace, subject only to the nominal overlordship of the steppe-dwellers. On other occasions, particularly when a new wave of migrants arrived from the east, Slav settlements were attacked and trade disrupted. The steppe separated the Slav agriculturalists of the forest zone from the Black Sea coast where numerous small towns had been established by Greek settlers as early as the second century B.C. and were now under the control of the Byzantine Empire.

Slav settlement at this stage was virtually confined to the mixed forest and wooded steppe zones, areas which offered a number of distinct advantages to the early communities. Although the soils were not, in their natural state, so fertile as those of the steppe, they could be used to produce crops of grain, to rear cattle and to grow flax for the manufacture of linen cloth. At the same time, the virtually unlimited supply of timber was a vital source of both fuel and building material for settled agricultural communities, commodities in short supply in the open steppe. Furthermore, the forests and marshes were a natural defensive barrier against the recurrent danger of attack by the pastoral nomads, who in any case would have little interest in occupying an environment so dissimilar from that to which they were accustomed.

From the earliest days, the Slavs' economy was by no means wholly agricultural; indeed some writers hold that agriculture was of relatively minor importance, at least in the early stages. The hunting of forest animals for their furs and hides and the collection of wax and honey were major activities and trade in these commodities soon became widespread. Here again, the mixed forest belt offered peculiar advantages. From the area to the west of the Moscow basin, the great rivers of the plain diverge towards the Baltic, Black and Caspian seas, their headwaters separated by short portages across low watersheds. These routes had been used in the days of Ancient Greece and were now revitalized by the eastern Slavs, who took a lively interest in the trade which flowed along them and particularly in contacts with Byzantium, via the Black Sea ports. A number of trading posts grew up along these routes and each became the centre of a loosely-defined Slav principality. Such were Novgorod, Pskov, Smolensk, Chernigov and Kiyev, all of them on or near the major routeway which ran from the Gulf of Finland via the Neva, the Volkhov, Lake Il'men, the Lovat and the Dnepr to the Black Sea. Novgorod, near the northern end of the route, and Kiyev, towards the southern limit of the Slav domain, became the most important centres and, for a while, rival contenders for leadership.

From the second half of the ninth century onwards, there was considerable infiltration into the Slav settlement zone of Scandinavian elements, known variously as the Varangians or "men of Rus", who came as warriors and merchants and stayed to rule. The advent of the Varangians coincided with a period when the Slavs were under pressure from the steppe peoples and when it appeared that the trade routes to the south might be cut. The newcomers succeeded in organizing the Slavs sufficiently to enable them to resist these attacks and individual Scandinavian rulers came to power in the various Slav principalities. In A.D. 950, these came together in a loose federation known as Kiyevan Rus, with Kiyev as its capital. The word Rus, originally applied only to the Varangian minority, now came to be used for the population as a whole and it is from this term that the word Russia is derived. As time passed, the Scandinavian element was in any case assimilated into the majority. Kiyevan Rus survived for some three hundred years, throughout which period it traded extensively with Byzantium (Constantinople). As early as A.D. 998, Vladimir, Prince of Kiyev, was converted to Christianity by missionaries from Byzantium, an event which won Russia to the Eastern Orthodox Church in contrast to the lands along her western border which were Roman Catholic. Monasteries and schools were established, art and literature flourished and Russia was, for the first time, strongly influenced by the higher civilizations of the Mediterranean. Although trade was a major element in the economy of Kiyevan Rus, this early Russian state also engaged in agricultural pioneering. Large areas of the wooded steppe were cleared and cultivated and the settled areas of the forest zones were much expanded.

Towards the end of the twelfth century, however, the power of Kiyevan Rus began to wane. Struggles for supremacy between the rulers of the various principalities, occasioned in part at least by growing pressure on land resources, weakened the confederation whose headquarters at Kiyev was dangerously exposed to attack by the nomads of the steppe. The thirteenth century witnessed the most devastating outburst of nomadic peoples from the east, that of the Tatars. Kiyev fell and was sacked in 1240, Kiyevan Rus was destroyed and the greater part of European Russia came under Tatar control as part of a vast Tatar-Mongol empire stretching from Eastern Europe to the shores of the Pacific Ocean.

The fall of Kiyev stimulated increased migration northward, a process which may be looked upon as a retreat by the Russians away from their vulnerable southern frontier into a zone of relative security. Protected by the barriers of swamp and forest from the ravages of the Tatar horsemen, the Russians led their own life, subject only to a general Tatar overlordship expressed mainly in the payment of tribute to the Khans. Over the years, the Russian population steadily grew and there was a sustained expansion of the area settled and cleared for agriculture. In such a situation, Russia was cut off from the mainstream of European civilization for more than two centuries. The Russian princes acted as tax-collecting agents for their Asiatic overlords and as such their authority over their own people was recognized and, indeed, encouraged by the Tatars, who often went as far as to allocate small bodies of troops to the various Russian rulers to assist them in collecting taxes. As a result, the power of the Russian princes increased until eventually they were able to assert their full independence from the Tatars.

One of the areas most affected by these developments was the district known as Suzdal', situated between the upper Volga and its tributary the Oka. Protected by strong natural frontiers of marsh, forest and river, Suzdal' attracted a particularly numerous population and soon became the most densely settled part of the European plain. At the same time, it was particularly well suited to engage in trade, lying as it did within easy reach of the headwaters of numerous navigable rivers. It was this area which became the heart of the Principality of Moscow (Muscovy).

As the wealth and power of Muscovy increased, its rulers gradually expanded its frontiers, gaining control over neighbouring, rival principalities either by treaty or by conquest. Muscovy was the first to assert its independence from the Tatars and thus took the lead in freeing European Russia from Tatar rule. By the sixteenth century, the ruler of Moscow was by far the most powerful of the Russian princes and in 1547 Ivan the Terrible was proclaimed "Tsar of all the Russias", setting the seal on his supremacy. Meanwhile the power of the Tatars had greatly declined. Not only had they lost control of most of the forest zone, they had also suffered from a good deal of internal strife and their domain had been split into a number of Khanates such as those of Kazan', Astrakhan' and the Crimea. At the same time they had lost territory in the west to the expanding Kingdom of Lithuania which had advanced south-eastward to the Black Sea, occupying, among other places, Kiyev itself.

Muscovy, as it emerged in the mid-sixteenth century, was the direct ancestor of the modern Russian state. It was hemmed in on all sides by rival powers: the Tatars to the south and east, the Lithuanians and Poles to the west and south-west and the Swedes, periodically penetrating across the Baltic, to the north-west. The history of Russia from this time forward may be considered as the process of expansion outwards from the core area of the Moscow principality (Fig. 14). Thus it is now convenient to examine this expansion in each direction in turn rather than to attempt a chronological description of the process as a whole.

THE EAST

The first stage of this expansion took place under Ivan the Terrible (1533–84). Striking out south-eastward to the middle Volga, he captured Kazan' in 1552 and four years later had extended Russian power to the Caspian Sea, taking Astrakhan' in 1556. The southern steppelands of European Russia were thus cut off from Central Asia by a belt of Russian-held territory along the Volga. In the ensuing hundred years, Russia devoted most of her attention to rapid expansion eastward into Siberia. Russian settlers had reached the western flank

A Geography of the Soviet Union

of the Urals in the thirteenth century and, by the sixteenth, had crossed to the eastern side, opening routes into the vast unexplored territories beyond.

Asia north of the Himalayas contains two very different geographical zones. In the south, high mountain ranges separate steppe and desert basins which were the homes of nomadic pastoralists and groups of oasis cultivators. To the north, covering the bulk of the area known as Siberia, were vast stretches of forest and marsh, occupied by numerous small, primitive tribes, engaged in hunting, trapping and stock-rearing with little in the way of settled agriculture. To the Tatars, these northern forests had been a forbidding area which they left strictly alone, but to the Russians they provided an environment which, though more harsh, was basically similar to that of their European homeland. Russian penetration of this zone, once begun, proceeded rapidly, meeting little or no resistance from the unorganized and ill-equipped indigenous peoples. The main lines of movement were along the great Siberian rivers, with occasional use of

FIG. 14. Territorial expansion of the Russian Empire and the U.S.S.R. from 1462 to the present. The inset shows recent boundary changes in the west. 1, Areas lost after 1913 and never regained. 2, Areas lost after 1913 and regained 1940–5. 3, Areas which have remained under Russian control throughout the present century (except during the two world wars). 4, Areas gained in 1945 which had never before been under Russian control.

the difficult Arctic Sea route between their mouths. Tobol'sk, near the southern edge of the forest, was the scene of the final defeat of the Tatars in 1587. The Russians reached the Yenisey in 1609, the Lena in 1630, Yakutsk in 1632 and Okhotsk, on the Pacific, in 1649. By the end of the seventeenth century, Russia was in control of nearly 2000 miles (3200 km) of the Pacific coast. The Russian penetration of Siberia bears many similarities to the opening up of the forested zone of North America. First came the explorers, closely followed by hunters, trappers, mineral prospectors and traders. As the area of colonization was extended and the indigenous peoples subdued, the new lands were taken over and organized by the State, which established military posts and provided garrisons and administrative personnel. Siberia also came to be a useful place of exile for criminals and political dissidents who were set to work in the mines, as well as a refuge for religious minorities and for small numbers of agricultural settlers freed or escaping from serfdom. It was not until much later, however, that Russian power extended southward into the wooded steppe and steppe zones of south-west Siberia, the most favourable area for agriculture, and large-scale peasant colonization did not take place until the nineteenth century.

In the far north-east, expansion continued virtually unchecked. Kamchatka and the Anadyr peninsula were annexed in the eighteenth century and the impetus of Russian exploration carried settlers across the Bering Strait into Alaska and southward along the eastern shores of the Pacific. These North American territories, however, were much too remote from the centre of Russian power ever to come fully under the control of Moscow and were finally abandoned in 1867 when Alaska was sold to the United States for $7,200,000, surely one of the best bargains in history.

Towards the southern limits of their Far Eastern domains, the Russians came into contact and conflict with rival powers. The Chinese Empire of the seventeenth century was expanding northward and was sufficiently powerful to put a stop to the southward expansion of the Russian Empire. In 1689, the Treaty of Nerchinsk fixed the boundary between the two roughly along the line of the Stanovy Mountains. With the decline of Chinese power in the nineteenth century, Russia was again able to expand. In 1858, the frontier was advanced to the lower Amur and in 1859 the area between that river and the Pacific coast was ceded by China. Vladivostock was founded in 1860. Sakhalin and the Kurile Islands were under joint Russo-Japanese control from 1854 until 1875 when, by an agreement between the two powers, Sakhalin passed to Russia and the Kuriles to Japan. From the mid-nineteenth century onwards, the main challenge to Russian expansion in the Far East was the growing strength of Japan and it was at the hands of the Japanese that Russia received her first major set-back. At the time of the Sino-Japanese War of 1895, Russia brought great pressure to bear on China, gaining a lease of the Kwantung peninsula (Port Arthur) and a "sphere of influence" in northern Manchuria. Between 1900 and 1904 much of Manchuria, in fact if not in law, was dominated by Russia, who was particularly interested in that country's industrial resources which appeared much greater than those of her own Far Eastern territories. It was, in fact, largely for control of Manchuria that the Russo-Japanese War was fought. This conflict resulted in a decisive victory for Japan, which established that country in the eyes of the world as a Great Power. Russia lost control of Manchuria, Port Arthur and the southern part of Sakhalin. The last of these was regained in 1945 together with the Kuriles, and Port Arthur was again leased from China until 1955. Manchuria, together with North Korea, in which the Russians at one time showed great interest, are now firmly within the Chinese sphere, the former as part of the Chinese Peoples' Republic and the latter as a close ally. Today, the Soviet Union and China, two of the world's largest powers in both territory and population, face each other along a frontier of some 2000 miles (3200 km).

Mention should be made at this stage of the Mongolian Peoples' Republic, formerly known as Outer Mongolia. This territory was within the Russian sphere of influence in the late nineteenth century but in 1911 became a province of China. In 1921 it became an independent Communist state and for the past forty years has had close economic and political links with Russia.

CENTRAL ASIA

We must now turn our attention to Russian expansion in a different direction, south-eastward from the European plain into Turkestan or Central Asia. South of the forested zone of western Siberia which, as we have already seen, came under Russian control in the seventeenth century, lies a fairly narrow belt of wooded steppe beyond which are the dry steppelands of northern Kazakhstan. These in turn are separated by the formidable natural barrier of the Central Asian deserts from the southern mountain zones which form the present frontiers of the Soviet Union. The foothills and basins of these mountains had, for many centuries before they came under Russian control, supported numerous populations, engaged mainly in intensive irrigated agriculture and organized into a number of Moslem Khanates centred on such ancient sities as Tashkent, Bukhara and Samarkand. Compared with the rapid Russian advance into Siberia, progress in this direction was slow. The wooded steppe belt was occupied during the seventeenth century and there were further small gains in the eighteenth, but as late as 1800, the frontier of the Russian Empire lay roughly along the present boundary of the Kazakh Republic. During the nineteenth century, however, the advance was much more rapid. The nomadic Kazakhs were no match for the warrior Cossacks who formed the spearhead of the Russian advance and, by 1850, the steppe and desert zones had been largely absorbed. The Khanates of the south now became the meeting ground of two spheres of influence, the Russian pressing southward, and the British reaching out from north-west India, each attempting to gain control of the area or at least to prevent it from falling into the other's hands. While the British confined their activities to political intrigue, the Russians mounted full-scale military expeditions across the desert and succeeded in subjugating the Moslem Khanates, despite the latter's attempts to maintain their independence by playing off one Great Power against the other. Tashkent fell to the Russians in 1865, Bukhara and Samarkand in 1868; and in 1888 an agreed frontier was demarcated between the Russian Empire and Afghanistan, the latter being supported by Britain as a buffer state on the north-west frontier of her Indian Empire. Some of the Khanates succeeded in maintaining at least a nominal independence as Russian "protectorates" well into the twentieth century. Bukhara and Khiva survived until after the Soviet Revolution, eventually joining the U.S.S.R. in 1920.

THE CAUCASUS

A rather similar series of events took place in the lands between the Black and Caspian Seas. Although the latter was reached by the Russians in the mid-sixteenth century, 200 years elapsed before they were established on the Sea of Azov; Rostov, at the mouth of the Don, was founded in 1761. At the end of the eighteenth century, the frontier of the Russian Empire lay along the northern flank of the Main Caucasian Range. The mountains themselves were the home of numerous small groups of Christian and Moslem peoples, fiercely independent and often engaged in fighting among themselves. In 1801, the Russians took control of the Kingdom of Georgia, when the last native king, George XIII, abdicated in favour of Tsar Alexander I, and parts of Azerbaijan and Armenia were annexed from Persia in 1828, but it took some fifty years of intermittent warfare before the last of the Caucasian tribes were overcome in 1864. The Russian frontier in Transcaucasia reached approximately its present position in 1878 and for a while extended westward to include the sea around Kars which was ultimately returned to Turkey in 1921.

THE EUROPEAN WEST AND SOUTH

The reader will have noticed that, between the Treaty of Nerchinsk in 1689 and the beginning of the nineteenth century, there was little expansion of the Russian domain in Asia. The intervening eighteenth century was in fact a period during which the attention of the Tsars was concentrated on their European frontiers and it was during the eighteenth and nineteenth centuries that these frontiers reached, and in places extended well beyond, their present position. Although Russian power had extended rapidly from its centre in Moscow to its most distant limits along the Pacific coast, there had been no simultaneous advance to the west or south-west. Russia, at the beginning of the eighteenth century, was isolated from the rest of Europe by rival powers and in particular had access to neither the Baltic nor the Black Sea. This lack of contact with the outside world does much to explain the backwardness of Russia compared with other European powers. She was, for example, virtually untouched by the Rennaissance or the Reformation which did so much to mould the modern civilizations of western Europe. West European traders and explorers, such as the Englishman Chancellor in 1550, made contact with Muscovy by the long and difficult sea route round the North Cape to Arkhangel'sk, itself separated from the capital by 600 miles (965 km) of forest and swamp. Contact with the Mediterranean via the Black Sea was possible only through Turkish waters.

During the reign of Peter the Great (1689–1725) the position was greatly changed. His victory in the war against Sweden (1700–21) resulted in the annexation of much of Latvia, the whole of Estonia and the lands around the head of the Gulf of Finland. Here, in 1703, Peter founded his "window on the west", St. Petersburg, which remained the capital until 1918. Peter the Great travelled widely in western Europe, including England, was much impressed by what he saw there and made strenuous efforts to modernize Russia. He imported foreign technicians to assist in the development of industries, especially metal-working in the Urals and shipbuilding at St. Petersburg, and founded the Russian Navy. At the same time he set about reducing the powers of the turbulent Russian nobility and overhauled the archaic administrative system. The highly centralized autocratic government which characterized the last 200 years of Tsarist rule was largely a product of Peter's reforms.

To the west and south-west of Peter the Great's Empire, a belt of territory from Lithuania to the Ukraine was under Polish control. The central Ukraine, the Crimea and the Black Sea coast were nominally part of the Turkish Ottoman Empire, though local power was often in the hands of Cossack chieftains. During the eighteenth century, these areas were brought within the Russian Empire. The capture of Sevastopol' in 1783 and Odessa in 1792 established Russian power along the northern shores of the Black Sea, a process completed with the annexation of Moldavia from Turkey in 1812. The western frontier was slowly advanced until, by 1800, it had reached approximately its present position. Advances beyond this line involved the annexation of Finland from Sweden in 1809 and the occupation of the Duchy of Warsaw as a result of the Vienna Settlement of 1815, which followed the Napoleonic Wars.

Russia's defeat at the hands of Germany in the First World War and her weakness in the period immediately after the Bolshevik Revolution resulted in large losses of territory in the west. By the Treaty of Brest Litovsk (March 1918), the whole of the Ukraine, much of Belorussia and the Baltic provinces were ceded to Germany, though the latter's collapse eight months later prevented the treaty from coming into effect. Nevertheless, the Soviet Union as it finally emerged in 1921 was a good deal smaller than the Russian Empire of 1913. A resurrected

Poland had pushed its frontier well to the east, Lithuania, Latvia, Estonia and Finland had become independent states and Bessarabia had been lost to Romania.

Growing Soviet power was accompanied by renewed westward expansion. The "winter war" of 1939–40 between the U.S.S.R. and Finland was followed by Russian annexation of the Karelian isthmus and frontier areas further north. The three Baltic states were incorporated into the Soviet Union in 1940 and Bessarabia and Bukovina transferred from Romania in the same year. Following the defeat of Germany in 1945, the frontier with Poland was moved some 150 miles (240 km) westward (roughly to the so-called Curzon line, the Russo-Polish frontier agreed by the Allied Powers in 1919). The northern part of East Prussia, annexed from Germany, part of former Polish Galicia and Ruthenia (the sub-Carpathian Ukraine), transferred from Czechoslovakia, were the only territories gained in 1945 which had not at some time been part of the Russian Empire, so that the U.S.S.R. today remains appreciably smaller than the Russian Empire at its maximum extent.

It is highly significant that the most important changes in the Russian frontiers during the present century have taken place in the west. Here, where no natural boundaries exist and where rival powers have faced the U.S.S.R. across the great plains of eastern Europe, a weakened Soviet Union was obliged to retreat in the years immediately after the Revolution, only to advance again as her strength was renewed. The smaller states of east-central Europe have been obliged to play the role of buffer states between the U.S.S.R. and the western powers. In the inter-war years their strongly anti-Communist governments were often supported by western European countries. In the post-war period, as Communist "Peoples' Republics" they have generally been aligned with the Soviet Union against the west. It is this western frontier which has been the danger zone for the U.S.S.R. since 1917 and events along this frontier have received most attention from the Soviet rulers. With the growing strength of China and the recent demonstration that her relations with the U.S.S.R. are not at all times completely friendly, we may expect to see more attention paid in the future by the Soviet Union to events along her Asiatic frontiers.

CHAPTER 4

THE PEOPLES OF THE SOVIET UNION

IN THE last chapter we saw how, by a process of expansion lasting some 400 years, the Russian Empire spread out from its original small nucleus in the Moscow basin to cover more than one third of Europe and nearly half of Asia. As a result of this expansion, many different peoples were brought within the boundaries of the Russian Empire, and the Soviet Union, inheriting the latter's widespread territorial possessions, also inherited its extremely diverse population. The various peoples of the U.S.S.R. differ in their racial, cultural, historical and religious backgrounds, and in the languages they speak. The census of 1959 recognized the existence, within the Soviet Union, of no fewer than 108 different national groups. Since the distinguishing feature of nationality is the possession of its own language, we can best examine the distribution of the peoples of the U.S.S.R. on the basis of linguistic groupings.

Many of the 108 nationalities are, of course, very small, no fewer than thirty-four having less than 10,000 members each. A further twenty-eight are between 10,000 and 100,000 strong and there are twenty-two of 100,000 to 500,000. This does, however, leave twenty-four sizeable groups of people, each numbering more than half a million. These are listed in the following table.

TABLE 1. MAJOR NATIONALITIES OF THE U.S.S.R.
POPULATION (000'S) AT THE CENSUS OF 1959

Russians	114,588	Germans	1619
Ukrainians	36,981	Chuvash	1470
Belorussians	7829	Latvians	1400
Uzbeks	6004	Tadzhiks	1397
Tatars	4969	Poles	1380
Kazakhs	3581	Mordovians	1285
Azerbaijanians	2929	Turkmen	1004
Armenians	2787	Bashkirs	983
Georgians	2650	Kirgiz	974
Lithuanians	2326	Estonians	969
Jews	2268	Udmurts	623
Moldavians	2214	Mari	504

The fact that these many nationalities live within a single political unit has, of course, made it possible for them to migrate and to become intermingled to a progressively greater degree, particularly during the present century. Thus,

50

LINGUISTIC GROUPS

RUSSIANS
UKRAINIANS
BELORUSSIANS
LATVIANS & LITHUANIANS

TURKIC
FINNO-UGRIAN
MONGOLIAN
MANCHURIAN

IRANIAN
CAUCASIAN
PALEO-ASIATIC
MOLDAVIAN

FIG. 15. Nationalities of the U.S.S.R. on a linguistic basis. Slav and Baltic groups are shown by red shadings, others in black.

individual groups are no longer restricted, if indeed they ever were, to clearly defined settlement areas of their own. Nevertheless, there are still particular districts in which one or other nationality is in a strong majority among the local population and such areas are generally recognized as the homelands of the various groups (see below, Chapter 5).

The present-day distribution of national groups within the Soviet Union (Fig. 15) is the product of historical processes already examined (Chapter 3) and of prehistoric migrations about which much less is known. The distribution is further complicated by the fact that the U.S.S.R. contains representatives of at least two of the world's major language families which now occupy areas of territory so intricately inter-mixed that it is impossible to draw a simple dividing line between them. The larger of these language families is the *Indo-European*, which originated somewhere between central Europe and central Asia and spread outwards to occupy a zone stretching from the Atlantic to India. The second and much smaller family is known as the *Ural-Altaic*. This, too, is a regional name indicating an origin in the steppe zone which stretches across south-west Siberia from the Urals to the Altai, whence it spread not only north-eastward through Siberia to the Pacific but also westward into Europe and south-westward into the Middle East.* As they spread out from their original centres, these linguistic families became differentiated into groups and the groups into individual languages, eventually resulting in the great diversity of tongues now spoken in the U.S.S.R.

THE INDO-EUROPEAN LANGUAGES

The largest representative of this family is the *Slav* group of tongues, spoken by more than three-quarters of the total population. By far the most numerous Slav-speakers are the **Russians** (Great Russians) who account for some 55 per cent of the Soviet people. Russians are in a majority over most, though not all the forest belt of Europe. Since it was they who played the leading role in the expansion of the Empire, they are also in a majority in areas which, before they came under Russian control, were quite thinly populated, notably a belt of territory running across south-west Siberia and along the southern frontier to the Pacific. As a result of continued migration, particularly to areas of recent agricultural and industrial development, Russians are now to be found in practically all inhabited parts of the country, particularly in the towns, where they form a small but influential minority of the local population. The second largest national group are the **Ukrainians** (Little Russians), with about 18 per cent of the total, who began to emerge as a distinct group from the thirteenth century

---

* The migrations which resulted in the diffusion of these early languages took place in remote prehistoric times when the physical environment of the regions involved was very different from that of the present day. Large areas which are now semi-desert, for example, were probably at that time steppe or even wooded steppe and offered no barrier to movement.

onwards. While the Great Russians, in their northward colonization of the forest zone, merged to a considerable degree with the indigenous Finnic peoples (see below), the Ukrainians, centred on the wooded steppe, received an admixture of Turkic blood as a result of the Tatar invasions. However, the Ukrainians remain basically European, speaking a Slav language closely allied to Great Russian. With the Russians they played an important part in the later stages of the colonization of Siberia where they are widely distributed, particularly in rural areas. The **Belorussians** (White Russians) are a much smaller group, accounting for less than 4 per cent of the Soviet population. They too are an offshoot of the original Slav stock, in this case much influenced by contacts with the Poles and Lithuanians to the west.

Another Slav group of significant size within the Soviet Union are the **Poles** found mainly in western parts of the Ukraine and Belorussia which were at various times under Polish control and where the population is a mixed one. The *Baltic* group includes two peoples, the **Lithuanians** and **Latvians**, whose cultures, including their languages, are quite distinct from those of the Russians. They have been much affected by contacts with the Poles and Germans.

Thus, even among the Slav majority in the Soviet Union, there is considerable linguistic variety, to which must be added differences in culture, particularly religion. Before the Revolution at least, the Slavs were all nominally Christian, but while the Russians, Ukrainians and Belorussians adhered to the Greek Orthodox church, a result of the conversion of Kiyevan Rus in the tenth century, the Poles and Lithuanians were Roman Catholics and the Latvians Protestants.

There are also a number of non-Slav, Indo-European peoples within the European part of the Soviet Union. In the extreme south-west, live the **Moldavians** of Bessarabia, linguistically allied to the Romanians, speaking a Romance language derived from Latin but adhering predominantly to the Orthodox church. It is perhaps surprising to find the **Germans** among the larger nationalities of the U.S.S.R. There was a considerable immigration of German-speaking farmers and artisans, often refugees from religious or political persecution, from the eighteenth century onwards. Before the Second World War, there was a sizeable concentration of Germans along the Volga River near Saratov. During the war, however, they were accused of collaboration with the invaders and dispersed to other parts of the country. There are very few Germans living in that part of East Prussia occupied by the Soviet Union since 1945. The local German population migrated to the west and was replaced by Russian settlers.

The number of **Jews** in the Soviet Union is much below its pre-war level as a result of German attempts at their extermination in the occupied territories. The majority of Jews, however, are still to be found in the European part of the country, though there are also small Jewish communities of very ancient origin in the Caucasus and Central Asia. The Jewish Autonomous Oblast (see below,

Chapter 5), established in the Far East in 1934 as a national home for Soviet Jews, contains less than 5 per cent of the Jewish population.

THE URAL-ALTAIC LANGUAGES

European Russia contains a number of peoples who speak languages belonging to the *Finno-Ugrian* subdivision of the Ural-Altaic family. These peoples were in possession of much of the forest zone before it was settled by the Slavs and although in many places they were assimilated by the latter, there are still areas where they remain a distinct group. Finno-Ugrian peoples are found in two main areas. In the extreme north-west of the country, they are represented by the **Estonians,** who have been much affected by contacts with German speakers, as well as the less numerous **Karelians,** who are closely related to their Finnish neighbours. A second predominantly Finno-Ugrian zone stretches south from the Arctic Ocean to the middle reaches of the Volga. The **Nentsy** occupy northern Siberia roughly between longitude 45° and 110°E. To the south of them are the **Komi** on the west side of the Urals and the **Khanty** and **Mansi** on the east. These are small and rather primitive groups. The **Mordovians, Mari** and **Udmurts,** however, who occupy an area stretching from west of the Volga to the flanks of the Urals, total nearly $2\frac{1}{2}$ million. Though Asiatic in physical appearance and retaining their Finno-Ugrian languages, these peoples are more advanced than their northern cousins. They are predominantly Orthodox Christian in religion and are for the most part settled farmers.

A second language group derived from the Ural-Altaic root is the *Turkic* whose speakers form the largest group in the Soviet Union after the Slavs, totalling well over 20 million. Moslem in religion, Turkic peoples occupy the greater part of Soviet Central Asia, where they are represented by the **Uzbeks, Turkmen, Kirgiz** and **Kazakhs.** As is the case with other Moslem peoples of the Middle East, these groups include both nomadic pastoralists and settled farmers, the latter now in the majority. Turkic speakers have spread out in several directions from their early homeland. To the west they have penetrated via northern Iran into the Caucasus (and, of course, into Turkey) where they are represented by the **Azerbaijanians.** To the north-west, the area between the Volga and the southern Urals is the home of the Turkic-speaking **Bashkirs, Tatars** and **Chuvash.** They have also moved north-eastward into Siberia. The **Khakass, Altays** and **Tuvinians** in the south and the **Yakuts** of the Lena valley and beyond also belong to the same group.

The peoples of Soviet Central Asia are Moslems. Most of them speak Turkic languages, but the **Tadzhiks** speak a language belonging to the *Iranian* subdivision of the Indo-European.

The Caucasus is a zone of extraordinarily complex linguistic patterns. A Turkic language is spoken by the Moslems of Azerbaijan, while the **Armenians,** who belong to the Gregorian Church, and the **Osetins** speak languages belonging to the Indo-European family. The other peoples of the Caucasus speak languages which are quite unrelated to either the Indo-European or the Ural-Altaic family. These languages also differ widely from each other, and their classification presents great difficulties. The *Iberian* group includes **Georgian** and several other closely related south Caucasian languages. The Georgians are Greek Orthodox and have a literary tradition dating back to the Middle Ages. There are literally dozens of other mutually unintelligible languages spoken in the Caucasus, especially among the various tribes of Moslem moutaineers living north of the main range. Among these we may note the *Circassian* group including **Cherkess, Abkhazian** and **Kabardinian** which have clearly marked similarities and the languages spoken by the **Chechen-Ingush** and **Lesghian** tribesmen which resemble neither the Iberian, the Circassian nor each other.

Mention should also be made of a number of Asiatic peoples whose languages are probably of Ural-Altaic origin but are distinct from both Turkic and Finno-Ugrian groups. The **Buryats**, concentrated in the Baykal region represent the *Mongolian* group. *Manchurian* languages are spoken by numerous small and rather primitive peoples of eastern Siberia and the Far East such as the **Evenki**. Finally, in the extreme east and north-east are the small groups often referred to as the *Paleo-Asiatics*, including the **Ainu** of Sakhalin, the **Koryaks** of Kamchatka and the **Chukchi** of the Arctic.

Enough has been said to indicate that the ethnic and linguistic composition of the Soviet people is extremely complex and that the pattern is difficult to describe in an orderly fashion. The diagram on page 56, while open to criticism, attempts to show the main relationships among the various groups whose actual distribution is illustrated by the map on page 51 (Fig. 15).

The larger national groups retain their own languages for official purposes and newspapers and books are printed in them. Russian, however, is taught in all schools and is becoming the second language of all educated members of the minority peoples. Some of the less important languages, spoken only by small numbers of people, are dying out and being replaced by Russian.

NATIONALITIES OF THE U.S.S.R. ON A LINGUISTIC BASIS

Indo-European

Slav	*Baltic*	*Teutonic*	*Romance*	*Iranian*	*Armenian*
Great Russians	Lithuanians	Germans	Moldavians	Tadzhiks	Armenians
Ukrainians	Latvians			Osetins	
Belorussians					
Poles					

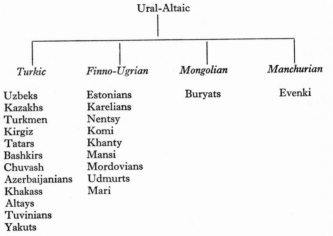

Ural-Altaic

Turkic	*Finno-Ugrian*	*Mongolian*	*Manchurian*
Uzbeks	Estonians	Buryats	Evenki
Kazakhs	Karelians		
Turkmen	Nentsy		
Kirgiz	Komi		
Tatars	Khanty		
Bashkirs	Mansi		
Chuvash	Mordovians		
Azerbaijanians	Udmurts		
Khakass	Mari		
Altays			
Tuvinians			
Yakuts			

Caucasian groups belonging to neither of the two major families: Georgians, Chechen-Ingush, Cherkess, Kabardinians, Abkhazian, Lesghian

Paleo-Asiatic groups: Ainu, Koryaks, Chukchi

Note. Only peoples mentioned in the text are shown in this table. Those omitted are, however, of little importance.

CHAPTER 5

THE ADMINISTRATIVE STRUCTURE
OF THE U.S.S.R.

OUR discussion, in the last chapter, of the linguistic composition of the Soviet people leads naturally to a consideration of the U.S.S.R.'s administrative structure since this is based, to a large degree, on the distribution of the various national groups. The country is divided into political–administrative areas of various kinds, the boundaries of which are intended to enclose the main settlement zones of the various national groups. These divisions are represented in the central organs of Soviet government; thus a brief description of the political organization of the country is relevant at this stage.

The highest legislative and administrative body of the U.S.S.R. is the *Supreme Soviet* which meets at least twice a year. This body elects a *Praesidium* which carries on the work of government between sessions though all its decisions are subject to the approval of the Supreme Soviet. The latter is divided into two chambers, the *Soviet of the Union* and the *Soviet of Nationalities*. The former is elected by the direct ballot of all citizens over the age of 18, and for this purpose the country is divided into electoral areas, each of which has some 300,000 inhabitants and elects one deputy to the Soviet of the Union. The Soviet of Nationalities, however, is elected on the basis of the various political units which make up the U.S.S.R. Each union republic sends 25 deputies to the Soviet of Nationalities, each autonomous republic sends 11, autonomous oblasts 5 and national okrugs one each. Since all measures must be approved by both houses, the Soviet of Nationalities, in theory at least, acts as a regulating body which ensures that the interests of the smaller groups are not overridden in the interests of the larger ones. For example, the Estonian Republic, with a population of only 1·2 million, sends 25 deputies to this body, the same number as the Russian Republic, which has over 117 million inhabitants.

POLITICAL DIVISIONS

The various types of political unit based on nationality have been named in the preceding paragraph. In addition, there are a number of purely administrative units which are based on economic rather than on ethnic considerations. Our next task is to examine the political-administrative structure of the Soviet

A Geography of the Soviet Union

Union and the relationships between the different units. These can be arranged into a series of levels of grades, units in the lower grades being subordinate to those at higher levels, the degree of local autonomy diminishing down the scale. The arrangement is shown schematically in the following diagram.

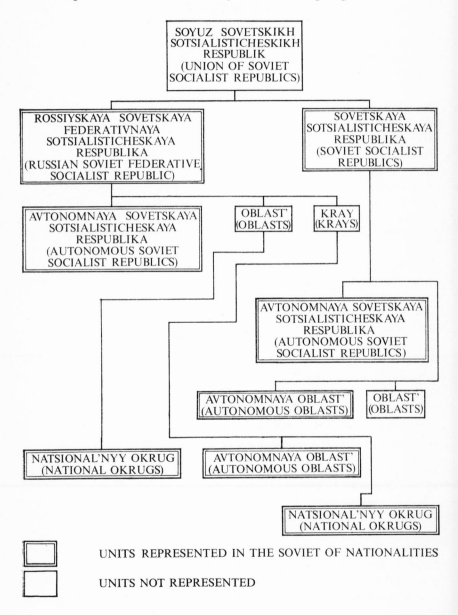

□ UNITS REPRESENTED IN THE SOVIET OF NATIONALITIES

□ UNITS NOT REPRESENTED

At the top of the tree are the full union republics, of which there are at present fifteen (Fig. 16). The Russian Republic, because of the large number of lower grade units within its boundaries, has been referred to as "a Union within a Union" and bears the cumbersome title of the **Rossiyskaya Sovestskaya Federativnaya Sotsialisticheskaya Respublika** (Russian Soviet Federative Socialist Republic (R.S.F.S.R.)). This covers the whole of the Russian homeland in Europe together with Siberia and the Far East where, as a result of the immigration of Russian settlers, people of Russian origin are in the overall majority. The other fourteen **Sovestskaya Sotsialisticheskaya Respublika** (Soviet Socialist Republics (S.S.R.'s)) represent the more numerous and more advanced minority peoples of the Soviet Union. However, because under the Soviet constitution, S.S.R.'s have the right to secede from the Union, each must have a frontier with the outside world. Thus a number of nationalities of considerable size, the Tatars for example, can never attain full S.S.R. status since their secession would create the "political anomaly" of an independent state completely surrounded by Soviet territory. The fourteen S.S.R.'s fall readily into three groups whose distribution reflects the pattern of nationalities already discussed. Six of them, the **Estonskaya** (Estonian), **Latviyskaya** (Latvian), **Litovskaya** (Lithuanian), **Belorusskaya** (Belorussian), **Ukrainskaya** (Ukrainian) and **Moldavskaya** (Moldavian) S.S.R.'s, lie along the western frontier. Three more, the **Gruzinskaya** (Georgian), **Armyanskaya** (Armenian) and **Azerbaydzhanskaya** (Azerbaijanian) S.S.R.'s are found in Transcaucasia, while Soviet Central Asia is divided among the **Kazakhskaya** (Kazakh), **Turkmenskaya** (Turkmen), **Uzbekskaya** (Uzbek), **Tadzhiskaya** (Tadzhik) and **Kirgizskaya** (Kirgiz) S.S.R.'s.

It is interesting to note that the federal nature of the Soviet Union is to some extent recognized in international affairs. At the United Nations, Belorussia and the Ukraine have seats and voting rights in addition to those held by the U.S.S.R. as a whole.

Subordinate to the S.S.R.'s are the **Avtonomnaya Sovetskaya Sotsialisticheskaya Respublika** (Autonomous Soviet Socialist Republics (A.S.S.R.'s)) of which there are at present twenty. These are widely scattered but there are certain regions within which they are particularly numerous. A group of A.S.S.R.'s in the area between the Volga and the Urals reflects the presence there of various Finno-Ugrian and Turkic minorities. The presence of numerous A.S.S.R.'s in the Caucasus is a further indication of the mixed composition of the population of that area. Other autonomous republica are to be found in Central Asia and southern Siberia.

Those parts of the R.S.F.S.R. which do not have A.S.S.R. status, together with the larger S.S.R.'s are divided into *oblasts* and *krays*. These have no direct political significance—they send no representatives to the Soviet of Nationalities —but are purely administrative and economic in function. The oblast is the

POLITICAL – ADMINISTRATIVE DIVISIONS (JANUARY 1962)

BOUNDARIES OF SOVIET SOCIALIST REPUBLICS (NAMED)

AUTONOMOUS SOVIET SOCIALIST REPUBLICS (1–20)

AUTONOMOUS OBLASTS (21–28)

NATIONAL OKRUGS (29–38)

LITHUANIAN S.S.R.

LATVIAN S.S.R.

ESTONIAN S.S.R.

BELORUSSIAN S.S.R.

UKRAINIAN S.S.R.

MOLDAVIAN S.S.R.

GEORGIAN S.S.R.

ARMENIAN SSR

AZERBAIJANIAN S.S.R.

TURKMEN S.S.R.

UZBEK S.S.R.

TADJIK S.S.R.

KIRGIZ S.S.R.

KAZAKH SOVIET SOCIALIST REPUBLIC

RUSSIAN SOVIET FEDERATIVE SOCIALIST REPUBLIC

MILES

KILOMETRES

basic economic unit into which all but a few of the smaller S.S.R.'s are divided. Its boundaries are usually drawn to embrace a variety of economic activities, each oblast having both an industrial and an agricultural element. The administrative centre is usually an industrial town which gives its name to the oblast. The kray is found only in the R.S.F.S.R. It is similar in function to the oblast but is usually much larger in size and occurs only in areas which are relatively thinly populated or recently developed. The kray is more directly subordinate to the central government than the oblast, the latter having a measure of local autonomy in economic matters. At present there are only six krays, those of Primorskiy and Khabarovsk in the Far East, Krasnoyarsk and Altay in Siberia, and Krasnodar and Stavropol' on the northern side of the Caucasus. Oblasts and krays are divided into *rayons* and these in turn into urban and rural districts.

Returning to our consideration of political as distinct from purely economic units, we find a third grade below the level of S.S.R.'s and A.S.S.R.'s. This is the **Avtonomnaya Oblast'** (autonomous oblast (A.O.)) of which there are eight. In the R.S.F.S.R., these are few in number and are subordinate to krays. Elsewhere they are subordinate to S.S.R.'s. Finally, at the lowest level, are the **Natsional'nyy Okrug** (national okrugs (N.O.'s)), numbering ten. These are found only in the R.S.F.S.R. where they are subordinate either to oblasts or to krays. These represent the homes of many of the smaller and less advanced of the Soviet peoples and are particularly numerous in Siberia.

Fig. 16. Political-administrative divisions of the U.S.S.R. at the beginning of 1962. Sovetskaya Sotsialisticheskaya Respublika (Soviet Socialist Republics, S.S.R.'s) are named on the map in conventional English. The following is a list of the conventional English and vernacular forms: Armenian S.S.R. (Armyanskaya S.S.R.); Azerbaijanian S.S.R. (Azerbaydzhanskaya S.S.R.); Belorussian S.S.R. (Belorusskaya S.S.R.); Estonian S.S.R. (Estonskaya S.S.R.); Georgian S.S.R. (Gruzinskaya S.S.R.); Kazakh S.S.R. (Kazakhskaya S.S.R.); Kirgiz S.S.R. (Kirgizskaya S.S.R.); Latvian S.S.R. (Latviyskaya S.S.R.); Lithuanian S.S.R. (Litovskaya S.S.R.); Moldavian S.S.R. (Moldavskaya S.S.R.); Tadzhik S.S.R. (Tadzhikskaya S.S.R.); Turkmen S.S.R. (Turkmenskaya S.S.R.); Ukrainian S.S.R. (Ukrainskaya S.S.R.); Uzbek S.S.R. (Uzbekskaya S.S.R.); Lower grade-units are indicated by shading and key numbers: Avtonomnaya Sovetskaya Sotsialisticheskaya Respublika (Autonomous S.S.R.'s): 1, Karel'-skaya. 2, Komi. 3, Mordovskaya. 4, Chuvashskaya. 5, Mariyskaya. 6, Tatarskaya. 7, Udmurtskaya. 8, Bashkirskaya. 9, Kabardino-Balkarskaya. 10, Severo-Osetinskaya. 11, Checheno-Ingushskaya. 12, Kalmytskaya. 13, Dagestanskaya. 14, Abkhazskaya. 15, Adzharskaya. 16, Nakhichevanskaya. 17, Kara-Kalpak-skaya. 18, Tuvinskaya. 19, Buryatskaya. 20, Yakutskaya. Avtonomnaya Oblast' (Autonomous Oblasts): 21, Adygeyskaya. 22, Karachayevo-Cherkessskaya. 23, Yugo-Osetinskaya. 24, Nagorno-Karabakhskaya. 25, Gorno-Badakhshanskaya. 26, Gorno-Altayskaya. 27, Khakassskaya. 28, Yevreyskaya (Jewish). Natsional'-nyy Okrug (National Okrugs): 29, Nenetskiy. 30, Komi-Permyatskiy. 31, Khanty-Mansiyskiy. 32, Yamalo-Nenetskiy. 33, Taymyrskiy (Dolgano-Nenetskiy). 34, Evenkiyskiy. 35, Ust Ordynskiy Buryat Mongol'skiy. 36, Aginskiy Buryat Mongol'skiy. 37, Chukotskiy. 38, Koryakskiy.

The administrative structure of the Soviet Union is highly complex but at the same time is a great deal less rigid than that of many other countries. Boundary changes and regrouping of areas frequently take place, particularly in the case of oblasts and krays which are modified in response to changing economic patterns. Changes in the frontiers of the various political units are less common, but do take place: in 1963, for example, a considerable area of territory was transferred from Kazakhstan to Uzbekistan. As particular minority groups become culturally more advanced and economically more developed, they may move up the ladder of the political hierarchy. Thus the Tuvinskaya Avtonomnaya Oblast' (Tuvinian Autonomous Oblast) was recently raised to the level of an autonomous republic. Conversely, under special circumstances, political units may be dissolved by the decision of the Supreme Soviet. In 1944 and 1945, a number of A.S.S.R.'s suffered this fate, notably those of the Crimean Tatars, the Volga Germans and the Kalmyks and Chechen-Ingush of the north Caucasus, on the grounds that their inhabitants had collaborated with the Nazi

---

Fig. 17. Economic Regions.

A. *Economic (Planning) Regions in use until* 1957. 1, North. 2, North-west. 3, Centre. 4, Volga. 5, North Caucasus. 6, Ural. 7, West Siberia. 8, East Siberia. 9, Far East. 10, Baltic Republics. 11, Belorussia. 12, Ukraine and Moldavia. 13, Transcaucasian Republics. 14, Kazakhstan. 15, Central Asian Republics.

B. *Economic (Planning) Regions established in the summer of* 1961. Subordinate to these were the 105 *Sovnarkhoz* (industrial–management) regions established in 1957 (see text). The economic regions shown here (Fig. 17B) form the basis of many of the maps and tables in this book. 1, North-west. 2, Centre. 3, Volga–Vyatka. 4, Central Black Earth. 5, Volga. 6, North Caucasus. 7, Ural. 8, West Siberia. 9, East Siberia. 10, Far East. 11, Donetz–Dnepr. 12, South-west. 13, South. 14, West. 15, Transcaucasia. 16, Kazakhstan. 17, Central Asia. Belorussia (a) and Moldavia (b) remained outside this scheme.

C. *Economic (industrial–management) regions announced early in* 1963. These supersede both the *Sovnarkhoz* regions and the planning regions shown in Fig. 17B. Although no data on the basis of these new regions appear in this book, they are mapped here for future reference since they are likely to be used for both industrial–management and long-range planning purposes for some time to come. 1, Upper Volga (Ivanovo). 2, Volga–Vyatka (Gor'kiy). 3, East Siberia (Irkutsk). 4, Far East (Vladivostok). 5, West Siberia (Novosibirsk). 6, West Urals (Perm'). 7, Komi (Syktyvkar). 8, Krasnoyarsk. 9, Kuzbass (Kemerovo). 10, Leningrad. 11, Moscow City. 12, Moscow Region. 13, Murmansk. 14, Lower Volga (Volgograd). 15, Volga (Saratov). 16, Oka (Tula). 17, North-east (Magadan). 18, North-west (Arkhangel'sk). 19, North Caucasus (Rostov). 20, Middle Volga (Kuybyshev). 21, Middle Urals (Sverdlovsk). 22, Khabarovsk. 23, Central Black Earth (Voronezh). 24, South Urals (Chelyabinsk). 25, Donetsk. 26, Kiyev. 27, L'vov. 28, Podolian (Vinnitsa). 29, Dnepr Dnepropetrovsk). 30, Kharkov. 31, Black Sea (Odessa). 32, Belorussian (Minsk). 33, Central Asian (Tashkent). 34, Alma-Ata. 35, East Kazakhstan (Ust'-Kamenogorsk). 36, West Kazakhstan (Aktyubinsk). 37, Karaganda. 38, Semipalatinsk. 39, Virgin Lands (Tselinograd). 40, South Kazakhstan (Chimkent). 41, Georgia (Tbilisi). 42, Azerbaijan (Baku). 43, Lithuania (Vilnius). 44, Moldavia (Kishinev). 45, Latvia (Riga). 46, Armenia (Yerevan). 47. Estonia (Tallinn).

invaders. Since the death of Stalin, the last two have been re-established. There is also one case of the demotion of a full Union Republic. The former Karelo-Finnish S.S.R. is now an A.S.S.R. within the Russian Republic.

From what has been said in this chapter it will be realized that to speak of the Soviet Union as "Russia" and to refer to its inhabitants *en masse* as "Russians" is as wrong as to refer to the United Kingdom as "England" and to label all its people "English". While it is true that the Russians are by far the biggest group

ECONOMIC REGIONS

A

BEFORE 1957

B

1961

C

1963

within the U.S.S.R. and that their republic is the largest political unit, it must be remembered that nearly half the Soviet people are *not* Russians and about one-quarter are not even Slavs.

ECONOMIC REGIONS

Mention has already been made of oblasts and krays as economic divisions of the U.S.S.R. which also have administrative functions as areas of local government. The subject of economic regions must be pursued a little further since these form the basis for Soviet planning and development and are widely used in published statistics. Each economic region is made up of a number of administrative areas which are grouped together. The boundaries of economic regions never cut across political boundaries and this has led to a number of anomalies of which the splitting of the Donbass coal-field between two economic regions is the most obvious. There is a certain conflict here between the recognition, in the Soviet form of government, of the existence of national groups and the desire to develop a logical pattern of economic regions.

Since 1957, important changes have taken place in the number and arrangement of economic regions (Fig. 17) but before examining the present situation we must take note of the state of affairs prior to 1957 since the great bulk of statistical information which is available is given on that basis. There were fifteen major regions (Fig. 17A). The R.S.F.S.R. was divided into nine: North, North-west, Centre, Volga, North Caucasus, Ural, West Siberia, East Siberia and Far East. The Ukraine (with Moldavia), Belorussia and Kazakhstan were economic regions in their own right while the smaller republics were grouped to form the Baltic, Transcaucasian and Central Asian regions. Within each of these major regions, oblasts, krays and A.S.S.R.'s were subordinate economic units with rather limited powers. In 1957, a new type of economic administrative body, the *Sovnarkhoz* (National Economic Council), was established and the country was divided into 105 *Sovnarkhoz* regions. For the most part, these were co-incident with the former oblasts, krays and A.S.S.R.'s, though in a few cases they consisted of a grouping of several oblasts. These new units had greatly increased powers in the economic sphere. Whereas their predecessors controlled only agriculture and industries considered to be of local significance, each *Sovnarkhoz* controlled all industry within its area including major projects of national importance formerly under the direct control of the central government. The establishment of the *Sovnarkhoz* system was a product of the marked trend towards decentralization of the Soviet economy which has been a feature of the post-Stalin period. The establishment of the *Sovnarkhoz* did not, however, mean the abolition of the major economic regions. These were retained as planning regions for matters concerned with broad, long-term aspects of economic development. The boundaries of these regions were extensively redrawn in 1961 and form the basis of statistical data published for 1961 and 1962. Since most of the figures used in this book are derived from Soviet publications of those years, the 1961 regions are illustrated in Fig. 17B. Early in 1963, a further change took place when *Sovnarkhoz* and planning regions were consolidated into forty-seven industrial management regions (Fig. 17c). These are intended to combine the functions of day-to-day industrial management and long-term economic planning. Though this change is too recent to affect the way in which data are set out in this book, it may be assumed that future statistical information will be published on the basis of this new regional division of the country.

CHAPTER 6

AGRICULTURE

GENERAL BACKGROUND

A great deal of the territory of the Soviet Union is highly unfavourable for agricultural development, mainly for climatic reasons. As we have already seen (Chapter 2), the high latitudes in which most of the country is situated, together with its land-locked character, result in a predominance of extreme continental conditions, characterized by intense winter cold and a short growing season. Large areas are, to all intents and purposes, useless for agriculture as a result. In addition, there are vast stretches of desert where, although the growing season is much longer, agriculture can only be carried on if water is supplied by irrigation works, a costly process. Further areas are marginal by reason of their low and unreliable rainfall. The Soviet policy of attaining self-sufficiency in food and other agricultural products has meant that many essential crops have to be grown in areas of climatic difficulty, a fact which considerably increases production costs. The short growing season characteristic of so much of the U.S.S.R. is an additional factor in raising costs, in that it demands the intensive use of a large labour force and much machinery during a restricted part of the year while these resources are under-utilized throughout the winter months.

The basic facts concerning land use are apparent from the following figures:

TABLE 2.

LAND USE (1961)	MILLIONS OF HECTARES	(ACRES)	%
Total land area	2227·2	(5501·3)	
Area in farms	1039·6	(2567·8)	47
Area used for agriculture	521·8	(1288·8)	24
Arable area	222·4	(549·3)	10
Sown area	204·6	(505·4)	9

The difficulties facing farming in the Soviet Union are clearly reflected in the fact that barely one-quarter of the territory is used for agriculture of any kind, while the area sown to crops is less than one-tenth of the total. The major uses of the sown area are as follows:

66

TABLE 3.

MAJOR USES OF THE SOWN AREA (1961)	MILLIONS OF HECTARES	(ACRES)	%
Total sown area	204·6	(505·4)	
Cereals	128·3	(316·9)	62·7
Technical crops	13·6	(33·6)	6·6
Potatoes and vegetables	10·8	(26·7)	5·3
Fodders and sown grasses	51·9	(128·2)	25·4

FIG. 18. Cereals. The heavier shading on each map denotes the main areas of production.

Particularly striking is the large area devoted to cereals, wheat alone occupying well over a quarter of the whole sown area. No other crop approaches it in importance. The generalized distribution of individual crops is shown in a series of maps on pages 67 and 68 (Figs. 18 and 19) and their significance in the agriculture of different parts of the country is discussed in the section of this chapter which deals with agricultural regions (p. 72). Confining our attention for the moment to the more general aspects of land use, we may note the figures given in Table 4 which illustrates the great variations that exist between regions in the

FIG. 19. Other crops. The heavier shading on each map denotes the main areas of production.

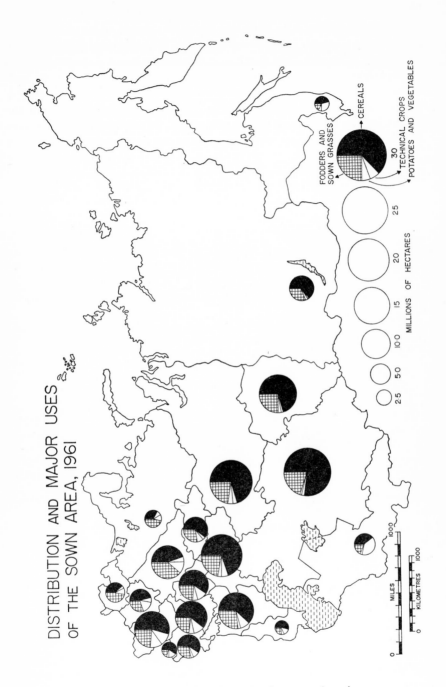

FIG. 20. Size and uses of the sown area by economic regions.

size of the sown area. The uses to which that area is put in each region are shown diagrammatically in Fig. 20.

TABLE 4. EXTENT OF THE SOWN AREA (1961) BY ECONOMIC REGIONS.*

MILLIONS OF HECTARES (ACRES)

Region	Total area	Sown area	Sown area as % of total area
U.S.S.R.	2227·2 (5501·3)	204·6 (505·4)	9·2
North-west	167·8 (414·5)	3·5 (8·6)	2·1
Centre	46·0 (113·6)	12·7 (31·4)	27·6
Volga–Vyatka	26·3 (65·0)	6·9 (17·0)	26·2
Central Black Earth	19·2 (47·4)	12·3 (30·4)	64·0
Volga	46·1 (113·9)	21·6 (53·4)	46·9
North Caucasus	43·1 (106·5)	16·0 (39·5)	37·1
Ural	225·9 (558·0)	21·3 (52·6)	9·4
West Siberia	99·2 (245·0)	17·7 (43·7)	17·8
East Siberia	722·6 (1784·8)	7·4 (18·3)	1·0
Far East	311·3 (768·9)	2·3 (5·7)	0·7
Donetz–Dnepr	19·7 (48·7)	12·5 (30·9)	63·4
South-west	29·3 (72·4)	14·9 (36·8)	50·9
South	11·1 (27·4)	6·5 (16·1)	58·6
Baltic S.S.R.'s	17·4 (43·0)	4·8 (11·9)	27·6
Transcaucasian S.S.R.'s	18·7 (46·2)	2·3 (5·7)	12·3
Kazakhstan	275·6 (680·7)	28·6 (70·6)	10·4
Central Asian S.S.R.'s	123·8 (305·8)	5·5 (13·6)	4·4
Belorussia	20·7 (51·1)	5·9 (14·6)	28·5
Moldavia	3·4 (8·4)	1·9 (4·7)	55·9

* For the boundaries of these regions see Fig. 17B.

On the basis of the proportions of their total areas under crops, the nineteen regions listed above fall into a number of fairly distinctive groups. The three regions of the Ukraine (Donetz-Dnepr, South-west and South), together with Moldavia and the Central Black Region, stand out as districts in which the sown area is between 50 and 65 per cent of the total. To the east and south-east, in the Volga and North Caucasus regions, the proportion declines to 37 and 48 per cent respectively. Central and western parts of the European plain (Volga–Vyatka, Central, Baltic and Belorussian regions) have between 25 and 30 per cent of their land under crops. In West Siberia and Transcaucasia, the figures fall below 20 per cent and in Kazakhstan and the Urals they are little above the national average of 9·2 per cent. Central Asia has less than half and the North-west less than one-quarter of the national average. East Siberia and the Far East, the two largest regions, have 1 per cent or less of their territory under cultivation.

Fɪɢ. 21. Agricultural regions (for detailed explanation see text). B. Main areas of sugar-beet production. S. Main areas of sunflower production.

These two regions, which together make up nearly half the area of the U.S.S.R. have rather less than 5 per cent of the whole sown area.

AGRICULTURAL REGIONS

The division of an area as large as the Soviet Union into agricultural regions presents serious problems to the economic geographer, not only in defining the regions themselves, but also in showing them on a map. Soviet textbooks of economic geography divide the territory into agricultural regions, generally between twenty and thirty in number, each region being named after its most important product or products. Soviet atlases, in mapping these regions, generally do so separately for each major economic region; rarely does one find a single map showing the U.S.S.R. as a whole. For this book it has been necessary to compress the great amount of detailed information available from Russian sources and to present a much simplified picture of the agricultural regions accompanied by a map of the whole country. This map (Fig. 21) distinguishes four major agricultural zones, each of which is divided into several regions, the latter numbering eleven in all. It should be realized that each of these regions is by no means uniform and that there are considerable contrasts in the character of farming between different parts of a single region. It is felt, however, that the scheme presented here gives a reasonably accurate picture of the range of conditions to be found within the U.S.S.R.

The scheme is as follows:

ZONE I. *Northern areas of low agricultural value*
  Region 1. Reindeer herding, hunting and coastal fishing.
  Region 2. Forest exploitation, with small-scale agriculture.

ZONE II. *Main agricultural belt*
  Region 3. Cereals, flax and dairying.
  Region 4. Cereals, hemp, potatoes, cattle and pigs.
  Region 5. Wheat and livestock
    (a) western, more intensive type
    (b) eastern, less intensive type.

ZONE III. *Southern areas of low agricultural value*
  Region 6. Desert and semi-desert stock-rearing.
  Region 7. Mountain stock-rearing.

ZONE IV. *Southern areas of high agricultural value*
  Region 8. Horticulture, viticulture and tobacco production.
  Region 9. Sub-tropical crops.
  Region 10. Areas of irrigated agriculture.

Region 11. Main areas of "suburban farming"

(these occur in zones II and IV in association with the major urban agglomerations).

It will be observed that there is a close correlation between the four agricultural zones and the major natural regions discussed in Chapter 2. Zone I coincides fairly closely with the extent of the tundra and taiga; zone II covers the mixed and deciduous forest belt together with the wooded steppe and steppe; zone III is coincident with the great deserts of Soviet Central Asia and the massive mountains of the south; zone IV is most widespread in the fringing belt between the mountain and the desert. We will now discuss each of the eleven regions in turn.

Region 1. Reindeer Herding, Hunting and Coastal Fishing

Throughout this huge area, which covers nearly one-third of the country, agriculture is virtually non-existent and a considerable part of the small population is engaged in nomadic reindeer herding. The people and their herds range far and wide over the northern part of the region in search of grazing for the animals on which they depend for most of the necessities of life. In the brief northern summer, the best pastures are provided by the tundra vegetation, but in the winter there is a general retreat southward into the open northern part of the taiga. Those who are not nomadic reindeer herders are, for the most part, engaged in non-agricultural activities such as fishing, hunting and trapping, lumbering and mining. Even the last two are not at all well-developed in this region despite its vast resources of timber and minerals. In the absence of reliable transport links, these resources remote from the main centres of population and industry are as yet virtually untouched.

Set into this region, in the valleys of the middle Lena and its tributaries, is the livestock and arable farming area of the Yakut Republic. Here, more fertile soils support patches of steppe and wooded steppe and the hot, though brief, summers permit the growing of crops. Indeed, the Yakuts were one of the few indigenous peoples of Siberia to develop settled agriculture before the arrival of the Russians. Today the crops grown are cereals, including some wheat and barley as well as oats and rye, together with a variety of vegetables, but the emphasis is on cattle-rearing and there is a heavy dependence on natural pastures.

Region 2. Forest Exploitation with Small-scale Agriculture

As summer temperatures increase towards the south, the proportion of the land devoted to farming becomes greater. Cattle are raised and cereals, wheat as well as rye, oats and barley, are grown, together with potatoes and sown grasses.

Even in this region, however, as its title suggests, agriculture is of secondary importance to lumbering, mining and trapping. Areas suited to agriculture are small and scattered and farming is usually at its most intensive in the neighbour-hood of lumbering and mining settlements. As the map shows, this region is quite narrow in the Asiatic part of the country but widens out to the west of the Urals. This reflects the less harsh environment of the European part and the fact that forest exploitation and other non-agricultural activities are more widely developed in this section. Outliers of region 2 occur in a few areas further south, notably in the Poles'ye and in the Meshcherskaya Nizina (Meshchera Lowland) to the south-east of Moscow.

The two regions just described cover at least half the Soviet Union and are of little or no agricultural value. They certainly provide no food surplus beyond the needs of their scanty population and where occasional large towns do occur, Arkhangel'sk and Murmansk, for example, these rely heavily on food brought in from other regions.

Southward from this negative zone is the agricultural "heartland" of the U.S.S.R. (zone II). This is at its widest along the western frontier and narrows eastward into the interior. Beyond the Yenisey, it breaks up into a series of disconnected pockets or islands of agricultural territory separated by broad expanses of forest. The range of crops grown in this zone is very wide, regional variations reflecting important variations in the physical environment. Put in the simplest terms, the latter involve an increase in summer temperatures and a lengthening of the growing season from north to south and a decrease in pre-cipitation from north-west to south-east. At the same time, the density of settlement and the general intensity of land use fall off rapidly to the east of the Volga and the Urals. There are three major subdivisions of this zone, regions 3, 4 and 5.

Region 3. Cereals, Flax and Dairying

This region occupies the northern half of the mixed and deciduous forest belt, generally north of the latitude of Moscow (56°N.). Though precipitation is a good deal more generous and temperatures less extreme than in many other parts of the U.S.S.R., soils are rather poor. Bad drainage is generally responsible for this, since there is a large excess of rainfall over evaporation and relief is gentle. Soils are usually very acid as a result. The traditional cereal of the region is rye, of which there is still a large acreage, but the crop is slowly being replaced by wheat. Oats and sown grasses support large numbers of dairy cattle and there are extensive though rather low quality semi-natural pastures. Flax is another traditional crop of the region and is still widely grown. Since it is particularly exhausting for the soil it often occupies the most fertile areas. Potatoes, grown as an industrial crop as well as for animal and human food, have greatly increased in importance during the present century. In the western part of the region, in the Baltic republics, the area devoted to flax diminishes while that under potatoes increases. Larger areas carry root crops and sown grasses and stock densities are a good deal higher than in more easterly districts. Pig-rearing is a well-developed subsidiary activity in the west.

Throughout the region, much of the land has not yet been brought under cultivation and remains either forest or swamp. As might be expected, the undeveloped area diminishes from north to south. Whereas, along the northern fringes of the region, less than 10 per cent of the land is cultivated, in the south the proportion rises as high as 60 per cent.

Region 4. Cereals, Hemp, Potatoes, Cattle and Pigs

This region occupies most of the remainder of the mixed and deciduous forest belt. Its rather cumbersome title denotes a widening of the range of crops produced consequent upon higher temperatures and a longer growing season. Most of the region is well suited to agriculture and little of the natural forest cover remains. Natural pasture, too, is much less extensive than in region 3 and over large areas the arable acreage is 50 per cent or more of the total. Hemp replaces flax as the main fibre crop, an indication of warmer conditions, and sugar beet makes its appearance in the south, where it is grown in rotation with wheat. The latter is the main cereal in the south of the region, but in the north it is secondary to barley and oats. Potatoes are widely grown, together with a variety of root crops for stock-feeding. The stock are predominantly dairy cattle although, as in most areas where modern dairy farming is carried on, pig-rearing is an important subsidiary enterprise.

Regions 3 and 4 are areas of intensive mixed farming where the production of crops and stock-rearing are closely integrated. Though these regions are important as grain producers they are by no means as significant in this respect as the steppelands to the south which are, by a large margin, the country's most valuable cereal-growing area.

Region 5. Wheat and Livestock

This is the largest of the productive agricultural regions and its simple title conceals a good deal of local variation. It has, however, a basic unity derived from its close correlation with the wooded steppe and steppe vegetation belts and its extreme importance as a supplier of both grain and livestock products. A major subdivision of the area occurs along a north–south line roughly along the Volga and thence midway between the Black and Caspian seas. To the west of this line, the climate is a good deal kinder than it is to the east: winter temperatures are appreciably higher, the growing season longer and precipitation more plentiful. Settlement and agricultural development took place much earlier to the west of the Volga than to the east and population densities are much higher, even if we discount the great urban agglomerations of the Ukraine. Consequently the intensity of land use is greater and the range of crops grown is wider, hence the division made on the map (Fig. 21) into "western, more intensive" and "eastern, less intensive" subregions.

Wheat is, of course, the dominant crop throughout region 5, though yields per acre diminish rapidly towards the east. West of the Volga, winter wheat predominates, but spring-sown varieties become progressively more important east of the Dnepr. East of the Volga, winter wheat disappears entirely, an indication of the harsher climate. Other cereals are also important and, though secondary to wheat, are produced in large quantities. These include rye and oats in the cooler north-west, some maize in the warm, moist south-west and barley and millet in the dry south-east. By the beginning of the present century, considerable parts of the European steppe were showing signs of soil deterioration as the result of long-continued cereal cultivation, and in places, particularly in the drier areas, soil erosion had become a serious problem. To combat these dangers and to increase the overall agricultural production of the region, farming has been greatly diversified. Industrial crops, notably sugar-beet in the damper north-west and sunflower in the east and south (*B* and *S* on Fig. 21), have been introduced on a large scale as have root fodders and sown grasses. As a result, the number of cattle which can be supported has increased and output of meat and dairy produce has risen. In the moister areas especially in the Ukraine, stock, including pigs as well as cattle, are closely integrated into the arable farming system and there is little natural pasture. Eastward towards the Volga and southward into the Crimea, the proportion of arable land declines and there is a greater reliance on grazing. In addition to the crops already mentioned, there is a good deal of vegetable production, particularly in the vicinity of large urban centres, and in several districts fruit and vines are important. Irrigation is used in some of the drier, southern parts, based on water from the Dnepr and Don rivers. Generally speaking, there is little possibility of any large-scale expansion of the cultivated area in that part of the region lying to the west of the Volga. Most of the suitable land has already been brought into use and any future increase in production will depend almost entirely on raising yields from land already farmed.

The steppelands to the east of the Volga are, as already indicated, a region where land is used much less intensively. Throughout this part of region 5, spring wheat is the main crop. In the north, where rainfall is higher and more reliable, oats and rye are also important and dairying is widespread, producing a surplus for use in other parts of the U.S.S.R. Southward, as rainfall becomes more scanty, the proportion of cultivated land declines. Spring wheat takes up an increasing part of the crop land and stock, among which beef cattle and sheep are more important than dairy cattle, rely to a higher degree on natural steppe pastures. It is in this southern part of the region, straddling the boundary between south-west Siberia and Kazakhstan, that large areas have been brought under the plough during the last ten years in the scheme for the reclamation of "virgin and long-fallow lands". Rainfall here is marginal for successful wheat production and yields per acre are low. However, thanks to a high degree of mechanization in these new lands, output per worker is high. Production has, in fact, varied considerably from year to year and although on balance there has been a valuable addition to Soviet grain supplies as a result of the scheme, output in recent years has been a good deal lower than predicted. The 1963 harvest was particularly poor. It may well be that earlier levels of output represented a rapid exploitation of the accumulated fertility of the virgin lands, a process which cannot, by its very nature, be continued indefinitely.

Pockets of steppeland, and thus of wheat and stock farming, occur farther east along the southern boundary of Siberia. In the Far East, in the lowlands which run from Vladivostok to the upper Ussuri, the main cereal is rice and the most important subsidiary crop is soya bean, a reflection of the special climatic conditions of the area.

Region 5, like regions 3 and 4, is a mixed farming region. However, the part played by cereals is very much greater than in more northerly areas and the integration of stock and crop farming much less close, particularly to the east of the Volga.

Region 6. Desert and Semi-desert Stock-rearing

As rainfall continues to diminish and summer temperatures to increase southward, the vegetation changes from steppe through semi-desert to desert and arable land virtually disappears. Natural pastures become poor, indeed over large areas vegetation is practically absent and, as a result, stock densities are very low. This region is traditionally the home of nomadic sheep-herders, but under the Soviet régime true nomadism has declined in importance as a way of life. In the more favoured areas, fodder crops are grown to supplement the scanty natural grazings and permanent settlements have been established to house the population. From these, herdsmen set out with their flocks on their annual migrations which now follow regular circuits, returning eventually to the starting point. In any case, despite its tremendous size, this region makes but a small contribution to the Soviet agricultural economy.

Region 7. Mountain Stock-rearing

Steep slopes and severe climates limit the possibilities for arable farming in these areas, though stretches of cultivated land are frequently to be found in the valleys. Transhumance between low-lying winter and high-level summer pastures is still widespread. In the Caucasus, dairy cattle are now the most important type of stock, but in the mountains of Central Asia, which are much drier, the emphasis is on sheep with some beef cattle.

Region 8. Horticulture, Viticulture and Tobacco Production

This category includes a variety of areas of intensive cultivation benefiting from special local conditions. In Moldavia, vineyards are especially important and now account for about one-third of Soviet production. Fruit, vegetables and tobacco are also produced in large quantities. In the southern Crimea, particularly along the coast, a wide variety of fruits are grown, including peaches, apricots and figs as well as apples, pears and plums, together with tobacco and vines. Much the same can be said of the Caucasian areas falling into this category. Along the lower Volga, the presence of fertile alluvium together with the availability of irrigation water gives rise to a broad ribbon of fruit and vegetable production which contrasts vividly with the semi-desert on either side.

Region 9. Sub-tropical Crops

Though very small in size when compared with the other regions, these areas are extremely important in that they constitute the only parts of the country in which a combination of heavy summer rainfall and high temperatures permits the cultivation of sub-tropical perennial plants. This has become a region of intense specialization producing high value crops, the most important of which are tea, citrus fruits, tung nuts (a source of vegetable oil), tobacco, vegetables and maize.

Region 10. Areas of Irrigated Agriculture

These are to be found in the drier parts of Transcaucasia but reach their greatest extent in the Central Asian Republics where they occur in mountain basins, in the border zone between the mountain and the desert and along the river valleys which stretch out into the latter. The most valuable single crop is cotton, but these areas also produce large quantities of rice, sugar-beet, hemp, tobacco, vines and fruit. Lucerne, grown in rotation with cotton, encourages stock-rearing, with *Karakul* sheep as a major product. Returns per acre of land are high and large surpluses are produced for use in other parts of the country. This applies particularly to fruit, vines and tobacco and above all to cotton, practically the whole of the U.S.S.R.'s supply coming from these districts.

Region 11. Suburban Farming

This region consists of a number of scattered pockets of intensive agriculture in the vicinity of the large urban agglomerations, where vegetables and milk are the main products. These perishable, high value goods, which are difficult and expensive to transport, are produced close to their markets and the distribution of areas of "suburban" farming depends on economic factors rather than on any particular conditions of soil or climate.

AGRICULTURAL ORGANIZATION

Some of the most striking changes which have occurred as a result of the Bolshevik Revolution have been those concerned with the ownership and organization of agricultural land. In the nineteenth century, most of the farmland of the Russian Empire was in the hands of large landowners and although, in the fifty years preceding the Revolution, many large holdings were broken up, big estates remained a major element in many areas. In 1913, of a total of 367 million hectares (906 million acres) of agricultural land, 152 million hectares (375 million acres) or 41 per cent were in large estates owned by the royal family, the nobility and the church. The remaining 215 million hectares (531 million acres) were in the hands of some 20 million peasant families who held, on average, little more than 10 hectares (25 acres) each. Generally speaking, the peasant holdings were more intensively worked than the large estates and accounted for at least 70 per cent of agricultural production. After the Revolution, large holdings were expropriated and their lands distributed among the peasants. There followed a period of some ten years during which, although state and collective farms were set up in some areas, the bulk of the land remained in the hands of individual peasant proprietors. This, however, was only a temporary state of affairs and was fundamentally changed by the policy of collectivization, which was applied on a large scale from 1928 onwards. Under the new system, the land passed into the hands of two types of farm, the Collective Farm (*Kolkhoz*) and the State Farm (*Sovkhoz*). By 1940, virtually all farmland was worked by one or other of these organizations. Areas annexed by the U.S.S.R. as a result of the Second World War were organized along the same lines, the process being practically completed by the early 1950's. About 100,000 individual peasant farms survive, for the most part in remote areas where settlement is too dispersed for collectivization to be practicable.

The Collective Farm

In this case, the land which, like all land in the Soviet Union, is the property of the state, is leased in perpetuity to the collective as a unit and is worked under the direction of a committee elected by members of the collective. This committee organizes the use of the land and labour force of the collective, subject at all times to the requirements of state planning policy for agriculture. The collective owns all agricultural equipment and farm buildings and many of the livestock, but the members retain small plots of land and a few livestock for their own personal use. The income of the collective is its produce and all dues are paid either in kind or in cash derived from the sale of produce. The first charge upon this income is the collective's responsibilities to the state which include deliveries of produce at fixed prices together with various tax payments. These are followed by capital outlays, such as the purchase of equipment and the maintenance of

4

reserves of seed and fodder, and the running costs of the farm. Further sums are set aside for pension funds and cultural activities. Once these charges have been met, the remainder of the produce may be disposed of in three ways: by sale to the state or by sale on the open market, in which cases a cash income is available for distribution among the members, or the produce itself may be distributed among the members. Each member thus has an income which may be in the form of cash, agricultural produce or both. The produce he may retain for his own use or sell on the open market as he thinks fit. The size of an individual's income is determined by a complicated piece-work system based on the amount and nature of the work performed. This is evaluated in terms of "workday units" which take into account not only the time spent at work but also the actual amount of work achieved and the degree of skill required for a particular operation. The produce and cash available for distribution among the members of the collective is divided up according to the number of workday units accumulated by each individual. During the past five years, various changes have taken place in the organization of collectives. These have involved a reduction in the scale of taxes and compulsory deliveries to the state together with the introduction of a basic wage scale in place of the previous system of annual payments. The basic wage is, however, in the form of advances to be set against annual income.

The State Farm

As the name suggests, this is owned and operated by the state and its workers are paid employees as in other state enterprises. Here, too, the individual is allowed a small plot of land and a few livestock for his own private use.

Until 1958, there was a third element in the organization of Soviet agriculture in the shape of the machine–tractor station (M.T.S.). These owned and operated mechanical equipment such as tractors and combines which served the collectives in return for payments in kind. Thus the M.T.S. formed a channel through which a good deal of agricultural produce passed from the collective to the state. In 1958, however, it was decided to abolish the M.T.S., and their equipment was sold to the collectives which the skilled operators usually joined. A small number of M.T.S. have been converted into repair technical stations (R.T.S.) which act as service centres supplying repair facilities, spare parts and fuel. This change has resulted in a valuable addition of skilled labour to the collectives and has removed their need to pay for the hire of equipment and operatives. On the other hand, the collectives are now obliged to pay for the purchase, upkeep and operation of the machinery.

Important changes have also taken place over the past decade in the number and size of collective and state farms. The number of collectives, which in 1928 was about 33,000, reached a peak of 236,000 in 1940 but by 1950 had fallen to 123,700. Since the latter date there has been a further rapid decline to 41,300 in 1961. This reduction in the number of collective farms results from a policy of amalgamating them into larger units. In 1961, the average Kolkhoz had some 6300 hectares (15,500 acres) of agricultural land with a sown area of about 2600 hectares (6400 acres). Collectives supported 16·5 million families, approximately

TABLE 5. SOWN AREA (1961) BY TYPE OF HOLDING

MILLIONS OF HECTARES (ACRES)

	Sovkhoz	Kolkhoz	Private plots and allotments	Total
Sown area	87·3 (215·6)	110·6 (273·2)	6·7 (16·5)	204·6 (505·4)
%	42·7	54·0	3·3	100·0
Cereals	58·5 (144·5)	68·6 (169·4)	1·2 (3·0)	128·3 (316·9)
%	45·6	53·5	0·9	100·0
Technical crops	2·9 (7·2)	10·6 (26·2)	0·1 (0·2)	13·6 (33·6)
%	21·3	77·9	0·8	100·0
Potatoes and vegetables	2·0 (4·9)	3·8 (9·4)	5·0 (12·4)	10·8 (26·7)
%	18·5	35·2	46·3	100·0
Fodders and sown grasses	23·9 (59·0)	27·6 (68·2)	0·4 (1·0)	51·9 (128·2)
%	46·0	53·2	0·8	100·0

TABLE 6. NUMBERS OF LIVESTOCK (1961) BY TYPE OF HOLDING

(MILLIONS)

	Sovkhoz		Kolkhoz		Private plots and allotments		Total
	No.	%	No.	%	No.	%	No.
All Cattle	21·4	26·1	36·8	44·9	23·8	29·0	82·0
Cows	7·3	20·1	12·8	35·3	16·2	44·6	36·3
Pigs	19·3	28·9	30·1	45·2	17·3	25·9	66·7
Sheep	40·8	29·7	67·1	48·8	29·5	21·5	137·4
Goats	0·3	4·3	0·9	12·9	5·8	82·8	7·0

400 to each farm. There are, of course, great variations in the size of collectives from one region to another.

State farms are and always have been much larger than collectives and have continued to increase in number in recent years. In 1928 there were 1407 Sovkhoz and by 1950 the number had reached 4988. Between 1950 and 1961 they increased by some 66 per cent to 8281, much of this increase being due to the fact that the state farm was the form of organization used in the opening up of new lands during this period. In 1961, the average state farm had about 30,000 hectares (75,000 acres) of agricultural land with a sown area of some 10,500 hectares (26,000 acres). There are significant differences in the contributions made by the two types of farm to the various branches of agricultural production (Tables 5 and 6). State farms now account for some 40 per cent of the sown area. They also include 45 per cent of the areas under cereals and fodder crops but only about 20 per cent of those under technical crops, potatoes and vegetables. The part played by private plots of land held individually by workers on state farms and collectives or as allotments not forming part of farms is out of all proportion to their size. Although these plots occupy only 3·3 per cent of the sown area of the U.S.S.R., and account for negligible proportions of the land under cereals, industrial crops and fodders, they include nearly half the land devoted to potatoes and vegetables. Still more striking is the state of affairs with regard to stock (Table 6). Private plots support nearly half the dairy cattle, more than a quarter of the pigs and over one-fifth of the sheep in the Soviet Union. Such a situation would seem to support the belief that many peasant families devote a great deal of effort to work on their private plots, to the detriment of the collective's fields.

AGRICULTURAL PRODUCTION

It is only during the past ten years that data on agricultural production in the Soviet Union have become available in any quantity. This lack of information for periods prior to the 1950's reflects the fact, recently admitted by the Soviet authorities themselves, that the achievements of the régime in the agricultural sphere have been much less impressive than those in industry. Indeed, it would be fair to say that, until about 1950, the growth of agricultural output barely kept pace with population increase and the amount of food available to the Soviet citizen was little greater than it had been in 1913. Historical factors are in part responsible for this situation. The two world wars, the civil war which followed the Revolution and the forced collectivization of the 1930's all played havoc with agriculture. At the same time there can be little doubt that, in the planned development of the Soviet economy down to 1950, agriculture was neglected, receiving a relatively small share of the capital and effort devoted to economic development when compared with that which went into industrial expansion.

Since the early 1950's, the position has radically changed. Agricultural production has expanded more rapidly than ever before and the current seven-year plan (1959–65) aims at a continuation of this growth. The basic facts are set out in Tables 7, 8 and 9.

MAJOR USES OF THE SOWN AREA

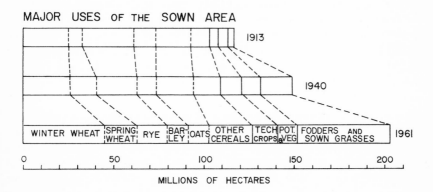

Fig. 22. Changes in the size and uses of the sown area, 1913–61.

TABLE 7. EXPANSION OF THE SOWN AREA, 1913–61

MILLIONS OF HECTARES (ACRES). (See also Fig. 22.)

(a) Area	1913	1940	1950	1961
Sown area	118·2 (332·0)	150·4 (371·5)	146·3 (361·4)	204·6 (505·4)
Cereals	104·6 (258·4)	110·5 (272·9)	102·9 (254·2)	128·3 (316·9)
Technical crops	4·9 (12·1)	11·8 (29·1)	12·2 (30·1)	13·6 (33·6)
Potatoes and vegetables	5·1 (12·6)	10·0 (24·7)	10·5 (25·9)	10·8 (26·7)
Fodders and sown grasses	3·3 (8·1)	18·1 (44·7)	20·7 (51·1)	51·9 (128·2)

(b) Index numbers. 1913=100	1913	1940	1950	1961
Sown area	100	127	124	173
Cereals	100	106	98	123
Technical crops	100	241	249	278
Potatoes and vegetables	100	197	206	212
Fodders and sown grasses	100	548	627	1,573

TABLE 8. INCREASE IN THE NUMBER OF STOCK, 1913–61.

MILLIONS. INDEX NUMBERS IN BRACKETS. (See also Fig. 23.)

	1913	1940	1950	1961
All Cattle	58·4 (100)	47·8 (82)	58·1 (99)	75·8 (130)
Cows	28·8 (100)	22·8 (79)	24·6 (86)	34·8 (121)
Pigs	23·0 (100)	22·5 (97)	22·2 (97)	58·7 (255)
Sheep	89·7 (100)	66·6 (84)	77·6 (84)	133·0 (148)
Goats	6·6 (100)	10·1 (153)	16·0 (242)	7·3 (111)

TABLE 9. AGRICULTURAL PRODUCTION 1913–61

MILLIONS OF METRIC TONS. INDEX NUMBERS IN BRACKETS.

(a) CROPS (BARN HARVEST)	1909–13 (av)	1940	1949–53 (av)	1961
Grain	72·5 (100)	95·5 (132)	80·9 (112)	138·0 (190)
Raw cotton	0·7 (100)	2·2 (315)	3·5 (500)	4·5 (643)
Sugar beet	10·1 (100)	18·0 (178)	21·1 (209)	50·9 (504)
Oil seeds	1·0 (100)	3·2 (320)	2·5 (250)	5·3 (530)
Flax	0·3 (100)	0·3 (100)	0·2 (66)	0·4 (133)
Potatoes	30·6 (100)	75·9 (249)	75·7 (247)	84·3 (275)
Vegetables	5·5 (100)	13·7 (249)	10·0 (182)	16·2 (295)
Maize for silage (incl. stalk and cob)	—	—	—	190·4

(b) LIVESTOCK PRODUCTS				
Meat and fat	4·9 (100)	4·8 (98)	5·2 (106)	10·0 (204)
Milk	28·8 (100)	33·6 (117)	35·7 (124)	62·6 (217)
Wool	192·0 (100)	161·0 (84)	198·0 (103)	366·0 (191)
Eggs (000 million)	11·2 (100)	12·2 (109)	12·9 (115)	29·3 (262)

As the above figures show, when the growth of population is taken into account, the supply of meat, fats, milk and grain available per head was no greater in the early 1950's than it had been before the Revolution. The number of livestock of all kinds (except goats) was appreciably below the pre-revolutionary level, though well above that of the 1930's. The sown area had increased by nearly a quarter, but the area under cereals had actually declined, the difference being accounted for by large increases in the areas devoted to industrial crops, veget-

FIG. 23. Changes in the numbers of livestock, 1913–61.

able crops and fodders. Output of sugar-beet, oilseeds and potatoes were all more than double their 1913 levels and production of cotton has increased fivefold. Flax, by contrast, was produced on a much smaller scale. During the 1950's, however, the area under cereals and the output of grain have increased rapidly but the most striking development has been the much greater attention paid to livestock farming. Over the past decade there have been large increases in the number of cattle and pigs and the output of meat, fat and milk has nearly doubled. The area under fodder crops has increased two and a half times in the same period. It is now the avowed intention of the Soviet authorities to catch up with the United States in the provision of these commodities: in the past, the Soviet farmer has devoted too much attention to cereal growing and the diet of the people has contained a high proportion of grain. Current trends will increase the protein content considerably.

The Soviet Union remains unique among the major industrial powers in the large proportion of her population actually engaged in farming. At present, agriculture occupies something approaching 40 per cent of the Soviet labour force compared with only 12 per cent in the United States. Though the U.S.S.R. may be overhauling other advanced countries in the output of food per head of the population as a whole it will be some time yet before she equals them in production per farm worker.

CHAPTER 7

THE DEVELOPMENT OF THE
SOVIET ECONOMY

THE Soviet Union has now been in existence for more than forty-five years and during that period the country has been transformed from one depending primarily on agriculture to the world's second greatest industrial power. The Soviet Union's achievements in the sphere of economic development have been very great and we should be unwise to delude ourselves by denying or minimizing this fact. At the same time, we should not make the opposite error of exaggerating the Soviet achievement and assuming that the rapid progress which has been made since the revolution is due solely or even mainly to the superiority of the Communist system over alternative economic and political systems. There is much truth in the assertion that economic development in the U.S.S.R. over the past forty-five years has to a large degree been a process of "catching up" with the more advanced industrial powers and that the vast changes which have taken place are indicative of the backward state of the country before the Revolution rather than a testimonial to the efficiency of Soviet planning as such.

There can be little doubt that the Russian Empire in 1913 could be described as backward, even underdeveloped in its economy, and that, as a result, the living standards of the vast majority of her population were low, much lower than they should have been in the light of the country's vast natural resources and the techniques then in use in other parts of Europe which might have been applied to the development of those resources. This is not to say, as is sometimes believed, that all industrial growth is a product of the Soviet régime and that no progress at all was made before 1917. In fact, the last fifty years of the Tsarist period witnessed a considerable growth of several sectors of the Russian economy. Compared with the expansion which has taken place since 1917, however, progress was slow and, what is even more significant, it was a great deal less rapid than that taking place in other capitalist economies during the latter half of the nineteenth century. The industrial revolution came late to Russia and by 1913 she was lagging behind the more advanced industrial nations by an amount which has been estimated at between thirty-five and fifty years.

Pre-revolutionary Russia was a predominantly agrarian country with more than 80 per cent of her labour force employed on the land. The vast majority of her people depended on agriculture for their livelihood and agricultural products made up a large part of her considerable export trade. She was one of the world's major wheat exporters and also sold abroad large quantities of flax, hemp, timber and furs. The fact that Russia was a large scale exporter of these primary products in itself suggests a backward economy in that, particularly in the case of grain, surpluses were only available because of the low living-standards of the people and their inability to consume these surpluses themselves. Similarly, the export of oil, metals and other industrial raw materials, which also took place, was indicative of a low degree of industrialization. The import of much machinery and manufactured goods was further evidence of the country's backward state.

The period between 1860 and 1913 saw expansion in a number of branches of industry and in a number of areas which have remained important to this day. During the fifty year period, production of coal rose from less than 0·5 million tons to 29 million, of pig iron from 0·4 to 4·2 million tons and of steel from practically nothing to 4·3 million tons. But this quite rapid growth still left Russia a long way behind other European countries. The U.K., for example, in 1913 produced 287 million tons of coal, 10 million tons of pig iron and 8 million tons of steel. Russian coal production was only 6 per cent of that of the United States and equivalent figures for other commodities were: oil 30 per cent, pig iron 13 per cent, and steel 14 per cent.

The limited industrial development which had taken place by 1913 relied heavily on foreign capital. The Russians themselves, even when they could afford it, had proved remarkably slow to invest in industry and at least half the investment capital had come from abroad, much of the modern equipment and many of the largest factories being in the hands of west European concerns. Management was generally far from efficient and the quality of the goods produced was low so that export was difficult and industry relied mainly on the internal market for the sale of its products. The general poverty and low living standards of the population resulted in restricted internal demand for manufactured goods, and this was a very real hindrance to expansion.

Industry was not only limited in the range of goods it produced, it was also very restricted in its geographical distribution. Heavy industry was confined almost entirely to the eastern Ukraine where the coal of the Donbass and the iron of Krivoy Rog were the main supports of the iron and steel industry. The Urals, which in the late nineteenth century produced the bulk of Russia's iron and which had, in the eighteenth, made her one of the world's leading iron producers, were, by 1913, an area of stagnation and decline. The Ural iron industry, which depended almost entirely on charcoal for smelting, could not compete with coke-smelted iron from the Ukraine, which was in any case closer to the main centres of population in the European plain. By the eve of the First World War, the Ukraine was producing nearly 70 per cent of Russia's pig iron and 56 per cent of her steel as well as 87 per cent of her coal. Another major development of the late nineteenth century was the exploitation of the Baku oilfield on the western shore of the Caspian. Large-scale extraction began here in the 1870's and by 1900 the district was producing 95 per cent of Russia's oil, almost half the world output. Even in this item, Russia's leading position was lost by 1910, as output rose more rapidly in other countries.

A large part of the manufacturing industry was situated in the region centred on Moscow. The traditional activities of metal-working, on the basis of local iron deposits, and textiles derived from the position of flax as a major crop in the area, were modernized and expanded from the middle of the nineteenth century. The Moscow region came to be Russia's main engineering district and cotton textile manufacture became a major activity. The latter depended on foreign, largely American, sources for up to half its raw cotton, the remainder coming from Russian Central Asia.

Away from the regions mentioned above, industry, apart from local handicrafts, was on a very small scale. The only centres of any importance were a few large cities and ports, notably St. Petersburg, Odessa, Arkhangel'sk and Batumi (an oil-refining and exporting centre linked to Baku by pipeline).

The fifty years which have elapsed since 1913 can be divided into a number of distinct periods. The First World War, which furnished striking proof of the economic and military weakness of the Russian Empire, together with the civil war which followed the Revolution, left the economy in ruins. The period 1917–20 is usually referred to as that of *War Communism* when the new régime in addition to its struggles with internal anti-revolutionary forces and their foreign allies, attempted to establish state control over all forms of economic activity. Industry was nationalized and the large estates of private landowners were broken up and redistributed among the peasants, who were charged with compulsory deliveries of foodstuffs to the state. The strain on the economy was too great and by 1920 both industrial and agricultural production, in virtually all fields, were still well below the by no means impressive levels of 1913. In an attempt to remedy this situation there was introduced, in 1921, the *New Economic Policy* under which a considerable return to private enterprise was permitted. A good deal of manufacturing industry was de-nationalized, private trading was encouraged and compulsory deliveries of food by the farmers were stopped. As a result, production began to increase in both agriculture and industry and by 1927 had returned to their pre-war levels. However, the experiment was short-lived. It was, of course, contrary to the principles on which the Soviet state was based and was a temporary expedient rather than a long-term change in methods on the part of the Soviet rulers. From 1925 onwards, private enterprise was subject to increasing restrictions and 1928 marked a return to full state control under the system of *Five-year Plans*. From that date onwards, as the Soviet constitution puts it: "The economic life of the U.S.S.R. is determined and directed by a State Plan of national economy with the aim of increasing the public wealth, of steadily raising the material and cultural standards of the working people and of strengthening the independence of the U.S.S.R. and its capacity for defence."

The first three five-year plans were for the years 1928–32, 1933–7 and 1938–42 respectively, the last being abruptly terminated by the outbreak of war with Germany in 1941. These plans were particularly concerned with the wider exploitation of the country's fuel and mineral resources, the development of the heavy industrial base, improvements in communications and the expansion of the engineering and chemical industries. Some idea of the progress made in these branches can be obtained from the figures given in Chapters 8 and 9. The concentration of effort and resources on the development of heavy industry meant, inevitably, that much less was done in other branches of the economy, that is in the production of consumer goods and in agriculture. The production of such things as textiles, clothing, foodstuffs, furniture and domestic equipment increased much more slowly and on the eve of the Second World War levels of output in these commodities were still very low by comparison with the situation in other industrial countries. The fifth five-year plan (1946–50) was devoted very largely to the reconstruction of war-devastated areas in the west where a large part of the Soviet Union's inter-war industrial capacity had been destroyed. The sixth plan (1951–5) brought renewed rapid expansion, again with the emphasis on heavy industry and much the same can be said of the seventh (1956–60). In 1957, however, planning targets were revised and a seven-year plan devised for the period 1959–65. While this still envisages that the most rapid rates of growth will be those in mining and heavy industry, it also aims at a more vigorous expansion in the output of consumer goods and foodstuffs than ever before. The effects of this significant change in emphasis are already to be seen in the rising standards of living of the Soviet people.

CHAPTER 8

INDUSTRIAL RESOURCES

THE Soviet Union is extremely well-endowed with industrial resources including both fuel supplies and most of the raw materials required by modern industry. The limited nature of the economic development achieved in the Tsarist period was a product of historical, social and economic factors and was in no way due to any lack of physical resources. Once a determined effort was made to carry out a full exploitation of the country's resource wealth and to build up the industrial side of the economy, it was almost inevitable that the U.S.S.R. should advance rapidly to achieve its present position as the world's second greatest industrial power. To give a complete list of Soviet raw material resource and their location would be a tedious exercise: reference should be made to such standard works as the *Oxford Economic Atlas of the U.S.S.R. and Eastern Europe*. In this chapter, attention will be concentrated on the distribution and development of major items and areas.

FUEL AND POWER

The U.S.S.R. is particularly rich in sources of power which are great enough to supply all her needs in the foreseeable future. The problems which do exist are concerned with the uneven distribution of these resources and the difficulties involved in exploiting them when they occur in thinly settled areas of harsh climate far removed from the main centres of population and industry.

Coal

This is the most important single energy resource in the Soviet Union. Estimates of coal reserves vary a great deal according to the method of evaluation used, but recent Soviet publications suggest a total of 8,760,000 million tons of which 7,765,000 million tons are classed as workable. Of these, 65 per cent are in the form of hard coal (bituminous and anthracite) the remainder being brown coal or lignite. However, of the total estimated reserves, only about 5 per cent are proven; 15 per cent are classed as "probable" and the remaining 80 per cent as "possible". Even the 5 per cent proven reserves are sufficient to support the present output for well over 500 years. The exact calculation of coal reserves is, of course, a highly complex matter and it is sufficient for our purposes to note

COAL BASINS AND DEPOSITS

LENA BASIN

TUNGUS BASIN

IRKUTSK BASIN

A

B

KUZBASS

PECHORA

URAL FIELDS

MOSCOW BASIN

DONBASS

KARAGANDA

GEORGIA

C

PRODUCTION 1961
(MILLIONS OF TONS)

A = EAST SIBERIAN FIELDS
B = FAR EASTERN FIELDS
C = CENTRAL ASIAN FIELDS

200
100
50
10
5
25
75
150

MILES

1000

KILOMETRES

1000

0

FIG. 24. Distribution of coal resources. Shaded areas are the main coal basins; black dots indicate smaller deposits. Circles indicate the volume of production from the fields named. For East Siberia, the Far East and Central Asia, circles denote total production from all sources in those regions.

that the Soviet Union's reserves are very large, probably as much as half the world total, and can supply all her needs for a long time to come.

Of much greater significance is the present situation as regards production and the contribution made to the total output by individual fields. The map of coal basins and deposits (Fig. 24) shows all known sources of coal, but many of these, particularly in the Asiatic part of the country, are virtually unworked. Included in this category, for example, are the vast Tungus and Lena coal-basins of eastern Siberia which together are believed to contain about half the Soviet reserves. Total coal production has increased more than nineteen times over the past fifty years, from 29 million tons in 1913 to 554 million tons in 1964 (Fig. 27). The contrast with the situation before the First World War is seen in the fact that, whereas in 1913, the U.S.S.R. produced little more than one-tenth of the United Kingdom's output she now produces more than two and a half times as much as Britain and rather more than the United States.

Soviet coal production is heavily concentrated on a small number of fields, four of which supply a large proportion of the higher grades of coal, including practically all the coking coal. These four, the Donbass, Kuzbass, Karaganda and Pechora fields, are considered to be of "all-Union" importance in that they provide large surpluses, over and above the requirements of local industry, for use in other regions. At present they account for some 60 per cent of the total output (Table 10). The remaining fields are generally of local importance only. They are usually poor in coking coal (e.g. the Urals) and in some cases a large part of their production is in the form of lignite (e.g. the Moscow basin). Some areas which appear as major producers in Table 10 are in fact composed of a number of relatively small and scattered mining districts (e.g. the Far East).

TABLE 10. COAL PRODUCTION 1913–61

MILLIONS OF METRIC TONS. FIGURES IN BRACKETS INDICATE PERCENTAGE OF SOVIET TOTAL.

	1913	1940	1950	1961
U.S.S.R.	29·1 (100·0)	153·2 (100·0)	248·9 (100·0)	510·5 (100·0)
Donbass	25·3 (86·9)	85·5 (55·8)	89·7 (36·0)	186·1 (36·5)
Kuzbass	0·7 (2·4)	21·1 (13·8)	36·8 (14·8)	84·9 (16·6)
Urals	1·2 (4·1)	11·7 (7·6)	32·2 (12·9)	63·4 (12·4)
Moscow Basin	0·3 (1·0)	9·9 (6·5)	30·6 (12·3)	36·8 (7·2)
East Siberia	0·8 (2·7)	8·5 (5·5)	15·1 (6·1)	36·5 (7·1)
Karaganda	— (—)	6·3 (4·1)	16·3 (6·5)	33·1 (6·5)
Far East	0·4 (1·4)	6·6 (4·3)	12·0 (4·8)	21·7 (4·3)
Pechora	— (—)	0·3 (0·2)	8·7 (3·5)	17·6 (3·4)
Central Asia	0·2 (0·7)	1·9 (1·2)	4·2 (1·7)	8·6 (1·7)
Georgia	0·1 (0·3)	0·6 (0·4)	1·7 (0·7)	2·7 (0·5)
Others	0·1 (0·3)	0·8 (0·5)	1·6 (0·6)	19·1 (3·7)

* Including Ekibastuz.

The Donbass, which has always been the most important field, still accounts for rather more than one-third of the total production, though this marks a decline in its relative importance over the inter-war period, when it accounted for more than half. The volume of production continues to increase, despite the difficulties presented by the rather thin seams which reduce productivity per worker well below the average for the country as a whole. The high quality of the coal, and the proximity of the field to major centres of population and industry have made it worth while to repair the great damage which occurred here during the Second World War and to continue the expansion of output from this field. Production from the Donbass has doubled in the last decade.

The Kuznetsk Basin (Kuzbass) is now the second largest producer, the output including a large proportion of coking coal. Productivity is high mainly because of the thick, easily worked nature of the seams: output per worker is nearly twice that of the Donbass. The Kuzbass was virtually unworked before the Revolution and its development on a large scale dates from the establishment in the 1930's of the Urals–Kuznetsk Combine, whereby Urals iron and Kuzbass coal were exchanged along the railways which join the two areas, thus assisting the development of heavy industry in both. With the wartime loss of the Donbass, the Kuzbass was for a while the leading producer. Output increased by 50 per cent in the war years. In the post-war period it has expanded even more rapidly, and by 1965 the Kuzbass is expected to supply 20 per cent of Soviet coal production.

The Urals coal-fields occupy third place in the volume of production, but this comes from a number of scattered, relatively small fields, organized into the four mining combines of Perm', Chelyabinsk, Sverdlovsk and the Bashkir Republic. Though output has increased rapidly in the war and post-war years, reserves are limited and no further expansion is envisaged during the current seven-year plan. Three-quarters of the production is in the form of lignite and there is very little coking coal. The industries of the Urals rely heavily on other sources, notably the Kuzbass and Karaganda, for this vital fuel.

The Moscow Basin is a good deal less important than its output would suggest, since the latter is entirely in the form of lignite. Expansion was rapid in the inter-war years and in the early post-war period, the aim being to lessen the dependence of local industries on coal brought in from other regions. Since 1950, however, the output from this field has increased by only 20 per cent, less than in any other region, and is expected to decline in the near future when there will be an increasing reliance on other forms of power.

East Siberia provides another example of recent rapid expansion. Of the numerous fields in this region, by far the most important is that of the Irkutsk basin, to the west of Lake Baykal. Current plans for the growth of heavy industry in this area will involve continued expansion of output from this field.

The Karaganda Coal-field began large-scale production in the 1930's when it supplied coking coal to the southern Urals. More recently it has supported major industrial developments in the Kazakh Republic. In view of the high quality of the coals and the fact that half of them are coking types, Karaganda ranks third in importance though not in volume of output.

The Far East contains a large number of widely scattered fields. The main producing areas are close to the Chinese frontier and in the island of Sakhalin.

The Pechora Field provides the only example of large-scale coal-mining in the Arctic and production costs are high. Output remained very small until 1941 when the loss of the Donbass stimulated the development of this remote field. Its exploitation involved the building of a railway some 800 miles (1280 km) long from Vorkuta to Kotlas, linking Pechora with the European industrial areas.

The Central Asian and Georgian Fields, despite a doubling of their output in the past decade, remain of minor importance. They are in fact exceeded in production by the small **L'vov–Volynsk Field,** transferred from Poland in 1945, which now produces nearly 6 million tons annually.

Despite the great developments which have taken place in the eastern regions of the Soviet Union, coal production and consumption, particularly the latter, remain highly concentrated in the European part of the country. Some of the most important industrial districts, notably the Moscow basin and the Urals, are poor in coal, which has to be carried in large quantities over long distances by rail. In order to lessen the strain on the transport system, Soviet planning has paid great attention to alternative sources of power.

Oil

This is by far the most important of these alternative sources of power and its production is now expanding much more rapidly than that of coal. Oil and natural gas together accounted for some 40 per cent of the energy produced in the U.S.S.R. in 1961 as against 48 per cent from coal. It is hoped that, by 1965, the proportions will have changed to 46 and 42 per cent respectively. Oil reserves are even more difficult to estimate than those of coal and numerous conflicting figures have been published. It seems probable, however, that the Soviet Union has larger resources than any other single country and that these amount to 26 per cent of the world total. This may be compared with 53 per cent for the Middle East as a whole, 13 per cent for North America and 6 per cent for Latin America. These figures are, of course, for known reserves and fresh discoveries may change the situation at any time. In contrast to the position as regards coal, known Soviet oil resources are heavily concentrated in the European part of the country (Fig. 25) which contains well over 80 per cent of total reserves. There are, however, distinct possibilities that large oil resources may be discovered in Asiatic Russia, particularly in western Siberia. At the moment, production comes mainly from three major areas, Baku and the north Caucasus, Turkmeniya, and the Volga–Ural district. The last-named, often referred to as the "Second Baku", is overwhelmingly the most important. Soviet oil production has increased very rap-

OIL FIELDS AND OIL PRODUCTION BY REPUBLICS 1961

SAKHALIN

BAYKAL

R. S. F. S. R.
134,540,000 TONS

KOMI-UKHTA

VOLGA-URAL
(SECOND BAKU)

KAZAKH S.S.R.
1,700,000 TONS

UZBEK, KIRGIZ, TADJIK
S.S.R.'s
2,146,000 TONS

EMBA

NEBIT DAG

TURKMEN
S.S.R.
6,110,000 TONS

UKRANIAN S.S.R.
2,837,000 TONS

NORTH
CAUCASUS

BAKU

GEORGIAN SSR.
31,000 TONS

AZERBAIJANIAN
S.S.R.
18,704,000 TONS

MILES   1000

KILOMETRES   1000

0

FIG. 25. Distribution of oil-fields and oil production. Shaded circles indicate the volume of production from each of the republics named.

A Geography of the Soviet Union

idly since the Revolution and continues to do so. The 1964 output of 224 million tons is not only nearly twenty-two times as great as that of 1913, it is also nearly five times as great as that of 1952. The continued expansion of oil production has been one of the most striking developments of the post-war period. Mention should also be made of an even more recent development; the output of natural gas, which in 1950 was only 6000 million cubic metres, exceeded 110,000 million in 1964. Major sources are those at Dashava and Shebelinka in the Ukraine, near Stavropol' in the north Caucasus and at various points on the Volga–Ural oil-field.

TABLE 11. OIL PRODUCTION BY REPUBLICS 1913–61

MILLIONS OF METRIC TONS. FIGURES IN BRACKETS INDICATE
PERCENTAGE OF SOVIET TOTAL.

	1913	1940	1961
U.S.S.R.	10·29 (100·0)	31·12 (100·0)	166·07 (100·0)
R.S.F.S.R.*	1·30 (12·6)	7·04 (22·6)	134·54 (81·0)
Azerbaijan†	7·67 (74·5)	22·23 (71·4)	18·70 (11·3)
Turkmeniya	0·13 (1·3)	0·59 (1·9)	6·11 (3·7)
Ukraine	1·05 (10·2)	0·35 (1·1)	2·84 (1·7)
Uzbekistan	0·01 (0·1)	0·12 (0·4)	1·71 (1·0)
Kazakhstan	0·12 (1·2)	0·70 (2·2)	1·70 (1·0)
Kirgizia	— (—)	0·02 (0·1)	0·42 (0·2)
Georgia	— (—)	0·04 (0·1)	0·03 (—)
Tadzhikstan	0·01 (0·1)	0·03 (0·1)	0·02 (—)

* Production mainly from Volga–Ural Field. Also includes north Caucasus, Komi–Ukhta and Siberian fields.
† Production mainly from Baku Field.

The Volga–Ural (Second Baku) Field is now the largest single producer. Though details of production from individual oil-fields cannot be easily obtained, data on output by republics are readily available (Table 11 above). From these it would appear that the Second Baku now supplies at least 70 per cent of all Soviet oil. The area was little developed before the Second World War. As late as 1940 its output was less than 2 million tons (6 per cent of the Soviet total); its present production is at least 130 million tons. It seems likely that this field will continue to provide the great bulk of Soviet oil for many years to come.

The Baku Field of Azerbaijan has a relatively long history of exploitation. It was producing on a large scale in the late nineteenth century and was the leading oil-field until the 1940's, supplying more than two-thirds of Soviet oil throughout the inter-war period. Since the Second World War, however, the importance of the Baku Field has diminished in absolute as well as relative terms. Most of the known reserves lie either at great depth beneath the ground or under the waters of the Caspian, making their exploitation both difficult and expensive.

FIG. 26. Oil and natural gas pipelines built or under construction in 1962.

Although new wells continue to be sunk, output is declining and the Baku Field now accounts for less than 12 per cent of total output. A further 8 or 9 per cent come from the north Caucasus fields, along the northern flank of the main range.

Until very recently, the **Emba Field** on the north-eastern shores of the Caspian was the only other producer of any importance. Even so, it never approached the Baku or Second Baku in output and although production continues to rise, it still provides only about 1 per cent of the total. In the 1950's it was outstripped by the rapidly developing **Nebit-Dag Field** of Turkmeniya. The bulk of the Ukraine's oil comes from the western frontier districts transferred from Poland after the Second World War, though there are considerable reserves in other parts of that republic. In addition to the districts already mentioned there is also small-scale production in Georgia, in the Fergana basin

FIG. 27. Changes in the production of coal, oil and electric power, 1913–63.

of Uzbekistan, in the Kirgiz and Tadzhik republics, in the Komi–Ukhta area of north European Russia and in the Pacific island of Sakhalin.

The uneven distribution of Soviet oil resources and the increasing emphasis on production from the Volga–Ural region leave large parts of the country, including many major centres of population and industry, devoid of nearby supplies. Consequently a major programme of pipeline construction has been carried out over the past decade and extensions are still taking place (Fig. 26). The most noteworthy item among current projects is the construction of pipelines from the Second Baku to Irkutsk with the possibility of ultimate extension as far as the Pacific. The massive expansion of output which has taken place since the war is placing the Soviet Union in a position where she may export oil on a considerable scale. Pipelines are under construction for the movement of oil overland to the countries of eastern Europe (the "Friendship" system) and to the ports of the Baltic and Black seas.

Minor Sources of Power

Coal, oil and natural gas together make up nearly 90 per cent of the energy produced in the Soviet Union (Table 12). The remainder comes from a variety of sources including hydroelectric power (see below), wood, peat and oil shale. With the exception of hydroelectricity all these have declined in relative importance in recent years, though the actual volume used has continued to increase.

TABLE 12. POWER SUPPLIES, 1913–61

MILLIONS OF METRIC TONS HARD COAL EQUIVALENT. FIGURES IN BRACKETS INDICATE PERCENTAGE OF TOTAL POWER SUPPLY. (See also Fig. 28.)

	1913	1940	1950	1961
All sources	48·4 (100·0)	240·8 (100·0)	318·8 (100·0)	764·6 (100·0)
Coal	23·1 (47·7)	140·5 (58·3)	205·7 (64·5)	370·1 (48·4)
Oil	14·7 (30·5)	44·5 (18·5)	54·2 (17·0)	237·5 (31·1)
Natural gas	— (—)	4·4 (1·9)	7·3 (2·3)	70·8 (9·3)
Hydroelectricity	0·2 (0·4)	3·1 (1·3)	7·6 (2·4)	35·4 (4·6)
Wood	9·7 (20·0)	34·1 (14·2)	27·9 (8·9)	26·0 (3·4)
Peat	0·7 (1·4)	13·6 (5·6)	14·8 (4·5)	19·6 (2·5)
Oil shale	— (—)	0·6 (0·2)	1·3 (0·4)	5·2 (0·7)

The quantities of material involved are extremely large. The production of peat, for example, used mainly for the generation of electricity, particularly in the Moscow basin, rose from 1·7 million tons in 1913 to 51·6 million tons in 1961, and that of oil shale from 600 to 15 million tons over the same period. The widespread use of these relatively low-grade fuels serves to emphasize the uneven distribution of coal and oil resources and the desire to reduce the costs involved in transporting them over long distances.

A Geography of the Soviet Union

FIG. 28. Changes in the sources of power, 1913–61.

Electricity

Soviet planners have paid a great deal of attention to the development of electric power and the total generated has increased from little more than 2000 million kWh in 1923 to 459,000 million kWh in 1964. Of the latter total, the great bulk is produced in thermal power stations, only 18 per cent being derived from hydroelectric sources. Hard coal is the most widely used fuel in power stations, but where this is in short supply, as in the Urals or the Moscow basin, for example, peat and lignite are used on a large scale. Oil and natural gas are of growing importance and as the pipeline system develops these fuels are likely to be still more widely used in electricity generation. Although hydroelectric sources still supply less than one-fifth of the electricity used, their exploitation has involved some of the most impressive pieces of engineering in the country. This is particularly the case where barrages have been built to tap the power of such major rivers as the Dnepr, Volga, Kama, Irtysh, Ob' and Angara. The stations at Kuybyshev (Volga), Volgograd and Bratsk (Angara), for example, have generating capacities of 2·1, 2·3 and 3·2 million kW respectively and together produce as much electricity as was derived from all sources in the Soviet Union thirty years ago. Such schemes as these are often multipurpose projects concerned not only with the generation of power but also, where appropriate, with the improvement of river navigation and the provision of water for irrigation purposes. The massive expansion of electricity production which has taken place in the U.S.S.R. is, however, by no means unique. Other countries, too, have greatly increased their output in recent years, and the Soviet Union is still a long way behind other major industrial nations in the availability of electric power per head of the population. In 1961, the total supply was equivalent to 1408 kWh per capita compared with 4803 in the United States and 2620 in the United Kingdom.

A major problem connected with electricity is its transmission from generating station to consuming area. Unfortunately for the Soviet Union, her greatest hydroelectric potential is in Siberia and the Far East, where the demand for power is as yet restricted. A number of large regional electricity grids, fed mainly by thermal generating stations are now in existence, notably in the Donbass, the Moscow basin and the Urals. It is planned to link these by means of a high voltage grid, which will also draw current from major hydroelectric plants along the Volga.

METALLIC MINERALS

With few exceptions, the Soviet Union is self-sufficient in metallic minerals. The distribution of the main worked deposits is shown in Fig. 29. Iron ore, the basis of modern industry, is widely distributed, but the bulk of Soviet production (which in 1964 reached 146 million tons), comes from a few sources. Of these, by far the most important are those at Krivoy Rog in the Ukraine and at various places in the Urals, the two regions together accounting for 85 per cent of the total output. Secondary producing districts of some significance are the Kuzbass and the Tula-Lipetsk area south of Moscow. The ore at present being mined is of high quality—the iron content is everywhere more than 40 per cent—and it has not yet proved necessary to work lower-grade sources. The U.S.S.R. is now one of the world's leading producers of chrome ore, mined chiefly in the Urals and northern Kazakhstan, and of nickel which comes mainly from Nikel' in the Kola peninsula and from the southern Urals. Nickel mining at Noril'sk, near the mouth of the Yenisey, is one of the few inroads so far made into the mineral riches of the Siberian Shield. Major deposits of manganese at Nikopol' in the Ukraine and Chiatura in the Caucasus support a Soviet production equivalent to nearly half the world total.

Non-ferrous metals are also in plentiful supply. One of the most important of these, copper, is mined at numerous sites in the Urals and Kazakhstan. The main sources of bauxite are in the Kola peninsula, at Boksitogorsk south-east of Leningrad, in the northern Urals and in Transcaucasia. Lead and zinc come mainly from the Leninogorsk district on the upper Irtysh but are also mined at several other places. East Siberia and the Far East are noteworthy as sources of gold and tin. Platinum, beryllium columbium, mercury and magnesium are all available in adequate quantities within the U.S.S.R. Unfortunately details of the scale of production of non-ferrous metals in the Soviet Union are not available, but there can be little doubt that she is a major producer of practically all the minerals needed by modern industry.

ECONOMIC MINERALS

A. ANTIMONY
As. ASBESTOS
B. BAUXITE
Ch. CHROME
Cu. COPPER
Fe. IRON
Fl. FLUORSPAR
G   GOLD
Gr. GRAPHITE
Lz. LEAD-ZINC-SILVER

M. MERCURY
Mc. MICA
Mg. MAGNESITE
Mi. MIRABILITE
Mn. MANGANESE
N. NICKEL
Pl. PLATINUM
Ph. PHOSPHATES
Po. POTASH
S   SULPHUR

Sa. SALT
T. TIN

0 100 300 500 MLS.

0 200 800 KMS.

Fig. 29. Worked deposits of economic minerals.

CHAPTER 9

INDUSTRIAL DEVELOPMENT

INDUSTRIAL development in the Soviet Union since 1917 has involved not only large-scale expansion of output but also major changes in the location of industry including its development in areas where it was previously non-existent. To see the effect of these changes we must now turn to a consideration of individual forms of industrial activity. Details of employment in the major branches of industry are given in the following table.

TABLE 13. INDUSTRIAL EMPLOYMENT, 1913–61, BY MAJOR BRANCHES OF INDUSTRY. THOUSANDS OF WORKERS. FIGURES IN BRACKETS INDICATE PERCENTAGE OF TOTAL. (THE FIGURES APPLY TO PRODUCTION PERSONNEL ONLY.) See also Fig. 30.

	1913		1940		1961	
Ferrous metallurgy*	307	(8·7)	405	(4·9)	923	(4·7)
Coal	196	(5·5)	436	(5·3)	1005	(5·1)
Oil†	51	(1·4)	45	(0·5)	154	(0·8)
Engineering and metal-working	510	(14·4)	2395	(28·9)	6207	(31·8)
Building materials	—	(—)	252	(3·0)	1375	(7·0)
Light industry	1133	(32·0)	1489	(17·8)	3472	(17·8)
Food industries	735	(20·8)	1049	(12·7)	1827	(9·3)
Others	604	(17·1)	2219	(26·7)	4585	(23·5)
Total	3356	(100·0)	8290	(100·0)	19,548	(100·0)

* Including ferrous metal mining.

† Extraction and processing.

The most striking change revealed by these somewhat incomplete figures is the overall growth in industrial employment which now stands at nearly six times its 1913 level although over the same period the total population has increased by only 60 per cent. Changes in employment structure were most marked in the inter-war years, when the numbers employed in engineering and metal-working (i.e. in the heavier branches of manufacturing) increased more than fourfold, while those in light industry and food-processing increased by only one-third. In the post-war period, although there have been big increases in

103

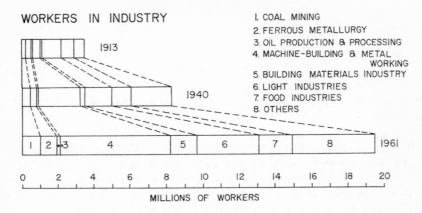

WORKERS IN INDUSTRY

1. COAL MINING
2. FERROUS METALLURGY
3. OIL PRODUCTION & PROCESSING
4. MACHINE-BUILDING & METAL
                           WORKING
5. BUILDING MATERIALS INDUSTRY
6. LIGHT INDUSTRIES
7. FOOD INDUSTRIES
8. OTHERS

MILLIONS OF WORKERS

FIG. 30. Changes in the number of workers in the major branches of industry, 1913–61.

the number of workers in all types of industry, there has been relatively little change in the proportions employed in the various branches.

THE IRON AND STEEL INDUSTRY

Despite the increasing importance attached to other materials, steel remains the fundamental basis of modern industry and the view that a country's economic strength can be assessed by its steel output is by no means obsolete. The Soviet Union is now the world's second producer: her output in 1961 (Fig. 31) was 70·8 million tons (U.S.A. 90·5) and her objective for 1965 is between 86 and 91 million tons. Some idea of the regional distribution of the industry can be obtained from Tables 14 and 15 which show the production of pig iron and steel by republics.

TABLE 14. PRODUCTION OF PIG IRON, 1913–61, BY REPUBLICS.
MILLIONS OF METRIC TONS. FIGURES IN BRACKETS INDICATE
PERCENTAGE OF SOVIET TOTAL.

	1913	1940	1961
U.S.S.R.	4·2 (100·0)	14·9 (100·0)	50·9 (100·0)
R.S.F.S.R.	1·3 (31·0)	5·3 (35·6)	22·8 (44·8)
Ukraine	2·9 (69·0)	9·6 (64·4)	26·4 (51·9)
Kazakhstan	— (—)	— (—)	1·0 (2·0)
Georgia	— (—)	— (—)	0·7 (1·3)

IRON AND STEEL PRODUCTION 1900-1962

FIG. 31. Changes in the production of iron ore, pig iron and steel, 1900–62.

106   *A Geography of the Soviet Union*

TABLE 15. PRODUCTION OF STEEL, 1913–61, BY REPUBLICS.

MILLIONS OF METRIC TONS. FIGURES IN BRACKETS INDICATE
PERCENTAGE OF SOVIET TOTAL.

	1913	1940	1961
U.S.S.R.	4·3 (100·0)	18·3 (100·0)	70·8 (100·0)
R.S.F.S.R.	1·8 (41·9)	9·3 (50·9)	39·9 (56·4)
Ukraine	2·4 (55·8)	8·9 (48·6)	28·0 (39·5)
Georgia	—	—	1·2 (1·7)
Azerbaijan	—	n	0·7 (1·0)
Kazakhstan	—	—	0·3 (0·4)
Uzbekistan	—	n	0·3 (0·4)
Belorussia	—	n	0·1 (0·1)
Latvia	0·1 (2·3)	n	0·1 (0·1)
Others	—	0·1 (0·5)	0·2 (0·3)

n=negligible.

The Ukraine

We have already seen that, in 1913 more than two-thirds of Russia's pig iron and well over half her steel came from the Ukraine. This region remains the most important though its relative significance has appreciably declined. It is still responsible for just over half the pig iron output and two-fifths of the steel and produces ten times as much of each commodity as it did in 1913. Its relative decline is due entirely to the growth of the iron and steel industry in other parts of the Soviet Union, notably in the Urals.

The iron and steel works of the Ukraine occur in a number of districts with different locating factors in each case. The most important (Fig. 32) are on the Donbass coal-field, the largest of them at Donetsk (formerly Stalino) and Makeyevka. In the nineteenth century, these depended mainly on local coal-measure iron ores, but now draw mainly from the vast deposit of high-grade ore at Krivoy Rog in the Dnepr bend. Once rail links between coal-field and ore-field were established in the late nineteenth century, interchange of coking coal and iron ore between the two areas began. This not only had the effect of stimulating iron and steel production in the Donbass but also resulted in the establishment of larger works on the Dnepr at Dnepropetrovsk, Dneprodzerzhinsk and Zaporozh'ye. A similar, though smaller scale, interchange between the Donbass and the Kerch ore-field in the Crimea led to iron and steel production at Kerch and at trans-shipment ports on the Sea of Azov, notably Zhdanov.

IRON AND STEEL INDUSTRY

FIG. 32. Distribution of the iron and steel industry.

The Ural Region

This is now the Soviet Union's "Second Metallurgical Base". We have already seen the region's importance as an iron-smelting area in the eighteenth century and noted its decline with the development of coke-smelting in the Donbass during the second half of the nineteenth. Charcoal continued to be the main source of fuel in the Urals industry until the 1930's, indeed some charcoal-smelting for the production of high-grade alloy steels still survives. However the significance of the Urals was radically altered during the first five-year plan with the establishment of the Urals–Kuznetsk combine. This involved the interchange of Urals iron and Kuzbass coal over a distance of some 1200 miles (1900 km). At a later stage, a similar arrangement was made with respect to the Karaganda coal-field of Kazakhstan. By 1940 the Urals had become a major steel area, producing about 20 per cent of the national total. The huge deposit of high-grade magnetite at Magnitogorsk is one of the largest single sources of iron in the world. A further stimulus to development was provided by the Second World War when the Ukrainian steel area was lost to the advancing German armies and the Urals carried the main burden of Soviet war production. There was a rapid increase in steel output from the region which has continued to expand in the post-war period. The Urals now turn out nearly 40 per cent of Soviet steel. Although new methods of coke production make it possible for Urals coal to be used in iron-smelting to a greater extent than in the past, the dependence on outside sources of coking coal remains heavy. The region produces only 2 million tons of coking coal annually but more than 12 million tons of coke. There are nearly a score of important iron- and steel-producing centres in the Urals: the biggest are at or near Magnitogorsk, Nizhniy Tagil, Chelyabinsk and Sverdlovsk.

Other Regions

The Ukraine and the Urals between them produce at least 85 per cent of Soviet pig iron and more than 75 per cent of the steel. Compared with these two regions, remaining districts are of relatively minor, though steadily increasing, importance to the national economy. These secondary districts have a variety of locational factors. The most important is the *Kuzbass* which, with its works at Novokuznetsk* (one of the biggest integrated plants in the country) and Gur'yevsk, produces about 8 per cent of Soviet steel. Formerly relying on Urals iron ore, the Kuzbass steel-works now draw much of their iron from recently-developed local sources. Coal is, of course, available in large quantities on the spot. The *Industrial Centre* (Moscow basin) obtains some iron ore from deposits near Tula and Lipetsk, where there are blast furnaces, but obtains much of its pig iron from the Ukraine. The steel-works, the largest of which are close

* Formerly Stalinsk.

to Moscow itself, depend heavily on scrap from local engineering industries to attain their annual output of some 3·5 million tons, 5 per cent of the national total. The much smaller production of the *Leningrad* district depends wholly on pig iron brought in from other regions and on local scrap.

The remaining republics account for less than 5 per cent of Soviet steel production. The plant at Temir-Tau, near Karaganda, which provides the whole of Kazakhstan's output is located primarily with respect to local coal and until recently depended on the Urals for its supply of iron. During the past decade, however, a number of important iron ore deposits have been opened up in the Kazakh Republic itself.

A number of steel-works have been established in various regions of the U.S.S.R. to supply the small local demand for steel, to support the growth of metal-using industries in those regions and to consume the scrap provided by local engineering works. Such pig iron as is used is usually brought in from other districts. Steel-works in this category are those at Begovat, near Tashkent, in Soviet Central Asia, and Komsomol'sk-na-Amure in the Far East. At Petrovsk, east of Lake Baykal, are steel-works of similar origin intended to support the growth of industry in the Irkutsk region. The presence of local coal and iron, together with current plans to establish a "Third Metallurgical Base" extending from Karaganda to Baykal seem likely to bring about accelerated expansion in this area. In Transcaucasia, the small supplies of coking coal in Georgia and the considerable manganese and iron ore deposits of the region support iron and steel production at Rustavi and steel-works at Zestafoni (in Georgia) and Sumgait (near Baku). Finally in at least one case, that of Volgograd, a major steel-works has been established on the basis of excellent rail and water transport facilities rather than on local resources of either iron or coal.

Numerous developments, some of them involving individual works of large capacity, have thus taken place in many parts of the Soviet Union. Impressive though some of these developments may be, we should not lose sight of the continued overwhelming importance of the two "metallurgical bases" in the Ukraine and Urals.

NON-FERROUS METALLURGY

As might be expected in a country possessing a great range of metallic minerals and aiming at industrial self-sufficiency, non-ferrous metallurgy is well developed in the U.S.S.R. Precise details of its scale and location are, however, difficult to obtain. In notable contrast to the position with regard to iron and steel, the Ukraine is not well represented in this branch of industry and the Urals are undoubtedly the most important region, being particularly concerned with the production of copper and aluminium. In the upper Irtysh valley, at Leninogorsk and Ust'-Kamenogorsk is the Soviet Union's second non-ferrous metal-working area where lead and zinc are produced on a large scale. These are also important at Ordzhonikidze in the northern Caucasus. Kazakhstan has major copper-smelting centres at Karsakpay and Balkhash.

ENGINEERING INDUSTRIES

Before the Revolution, the engineering industries of Russia were poorly developed. With the exception of shipbuilding and railway engineering, production was on a very small scale and most machinery was imported. The position has been greatly improved over the past 40 years. Engineering now employs nearly one-third of the Soviet industrial labour force and imports of machinery have fallen to a low level. In the Soviet Union today, as in all industrially developed countries, the distribution of the engineering industry is closely related to markets, that is to the manufacturing industries which use its products, as well as to sources of iron and steel, non-ferrous metals and power. The U.S.S.R. has been particularly concerned with the expansion of its heavy industrial base; consequently the heavier branches of engineering, producing equipment for the mining, metallurgical and power industries have undergone the most rapid expansion. Heavy engineering is most developed in the major industrial areas of the Donbass, Urals and Kuzbass. Another item of particular importance has been the production of transport equipment, especially railway locomotives and rolling stock. This branch of engineering is widely dispersed throughout the country, but the bulk of production again occurs in major industrial regions. More highly specialized and highly skilled types of engineering producing, for example, electrical equipment, machine tools and motor vehicles are heavily concentrated in the Leningrad–Gor'kiy–Moscow region, though they are by no means absent from other parts of the country. These activities, in the Industrial Centre at least, are based on a long tradition of manufacturing and a highly skilled labour force rather than on local physical resources. Agricultural engineering is a widely dispersed branch of industry occurring in all agricultural regions. The biggest works are usually found at sites having access to large supplies of steel and/or power; some of the most important being in the eastern Ukraine and in the great cities along the Volga such as Kazan', Saratov and Volgograd.

Although the various branches of engineering show concentration into a number of major regions as indicated above, the industry is represented, albeit on a small scale, in virtually all towns of any size. As one Soviet writer puts it, "clusters of machine-building enterprises have been created in all parts of the country, depending on the industrial specialization of the given regions; this is done with the aim of making the economy of the region more complete".

THE CHEMICAL INDUSTRY

This is a modern branch of industry which has made rapid strides in all developed countries during the twentieth century. Soviet progress in this sphere has, however, been rather less marked than in some other countries, for example in Germany or the United States. Expansion was relatively slow in the U.S.S.R. down to the Second World War, but in the post-war period the growth of this industry has been much accelerated. Compared with Soviet industry as a whole, the size of the chemicals branch is quite small and the production of chemicals is not a major specialization in any particular region. The great variety of raw materials used and the wide range of products make it impossible to identify a simple distribution pattern for the industry as a whole. Initial concentration processes usually take place near the raw material source but the final preparation of chemical products is usually carried out in market areas. These products include mineral fertilizers, sulphuric acid, caustic soda, synthetic rubber, dyes, paints, plastics and artificial fibres and pharmaceuticals.

Fertilizers

Phosphatic fertilizers are derived mainly from the apatite deposits of the Kola peninsula and, on a smaller scale, from phosphorite rocks in various parts of the country. The raw material is concentrated at source and transported to the agricultural consuming areas where the fertilizers themselves are manufactured in urban centres for local distribution. The basic raw material for nitrogenous fertilizer production is coal and this branch of the industry is carried out close to centres of coal-mining. The main areas are the Centre, the Ukraine, the Urals, and Uzbekistan. By far the largest source of potash used in the manufacture of fertilizers is the deposit near Solikamsk, on the western flank of the Urals. The output of mineral fertilizers as a whole has greatly increased in the Soviet period. Production of all types in 1913 was only 89,000 tons; in 1964 it reached 2·56 million tons. At the end of 1963, plans were announced for an accelerated expansion of the chemical industry and particularly of the fertilizers branch.

Sulphuric Acid

This has a wide variety of industrial uses. The raw materials used in its manufacture include coal in the Tula district, sulphur pyrites in the Urals, Transcaucasia, the Altai and eastern Siberia, and widely scattered sulphur deposits in the Central Asian republics.

Caustic Soda

This is produced mainly from deposits of common salt (sodium chloride) at Solikamsk, at Sol'Iletsk in the south-west Urals, Artemovsk in the Donbass and along the lower Volga.

5

Synthetic Rubber

Over the world as a whole, the main source of rubber is the rubber tree, *Hevea brasiliensis*, but this is not grown in the Soviet Union. Reliance on foreign supplies of rubber has been appreciably reduced by the cultivation of other latex-producing species, including *Kok-sagyz* (*Taraxacum kok-saghyz*), *Tau-sagyz* (*Scorzonera tau-saghys*), *Guayule* (*Parthenium argentatum*) and milkweed (*Asclepias*). The supply of latex from these plants, however, is insufficient to meet all Soviet needs, hence the growth of a synthetic rubber industry which is likely to expand at an accelerating rate as road transport develops. This industry depends mainly on ethyl alcohol distilled from potatoes. Manufacture takes place at Yaroslavl', Voronezh, Yefremov (Tul'skaya (Tula) Oblast) and Kazan'. Synthetic rubber is also made at Yerevan in Armenia, on the basis of calcium carbide derived from local limestone.

Dyes

Dyes for the textile industry are manufactured mainly from coal, the initial stages being carried out in the Donbass and the final processing in the Moscow basin textile area.

Paints and Lacquers

The chief raw materials, linseed and wood oils, are a product mainly of the Moscow basin but are also manufactured in Leningrad, Rostov, Kharkov, Odessa and the Kuzbass.

Plastics and Artificial Fibres

These are also produced mainly in the Industrial Centre.

Pharmaceuticals

These are made on a large scale in Moscow, Leningrad, Kharkov, Kiev, Chimkent and Baku.

Petro-chemicals

Detailed information regarding the size and distribution of the petro-chemical industry is not available, but in view of the rapid expansion in oil production that has taken place in recent years, there can be little doubt that this branch of the chemical industry is of growing importance, supplying a number of chemical raw materials previously found from other sources. While many oil refineries are to be found on the oil-fields themselves, thus giving rise to petroleum-based chemical industries near the sources of oil, the growing network of pipelines, together with the large-scale movement of oil by land and water are resulting in the establishment of refineries and petro-chemical industries in many other areas.

TIMBER INDUSTRIES

More than 700 million hectares (2,800,000 sq miles), nearly one-third of the total area of the U.S.S.R., are forest covered and timber is a major natural resource and export commodity. Industries based on timber employ more than 10 per cent of the industrial labour force. Of the 245 million cubic metres produced each year (10 per cent of the world output) almost one-third is still used for fuel, being particularly important in areas remote from sources of coal or oil. The remainder goes to paper-making and varied wood-working and chemical industries.

Although the great majority of Soviet timber reserves are now in Siberia, nearly three-quarters of the timber produced comes from the European part of the country, which is also the market for 75 per cent of the timber products. While the industry is located, in a general sense, in the market areas, individual processing centres are usually located where there are good transport facilities, timber being a major item carried by the railways and making up nearly half the volume of goods carried by inland waterways. The general arrangement is one whereby felled timber is transported to saw-milling centres from which the sawn timber is distributed to market areas. Saw-milling is thus carried on not only in many of the towns of the forested zone of European Russia and at a smaller number of centres in southern Siberia but also outside the forest belt at such places as Saratov, Volgograd, Rostov and Dnepropetrovsk all of which receive their timber by waterway. Such activities as furniture making, on the other hand, are more concentrated into a few large cities, the most important centres being Moscow, Leningrad and Kiyev. Paper production, one of the largest consumers of timber, is especially important in the North-west and Ural regions though the biggest single centre is at Pravdinsk, near Gorkiy, whence comes the paper for *Pravda* and other leading publications.

At the moment, there is a notable lack of balance in the timber industry between sources of supply and areas of demand. Both are mainly in European Russia, but are usually separated by long distances over which timber must be transported, thus greatly increasing costs. The rate of cutting in European Russia now exceeds that of natural growth by a considerable margin and it is intended to accelerate the exploitation of the huge Siberian reserves where current rates of cutting are equivalent to less than 10 per cent of the natural growth rate. The movement of the industry eastward across the Urals will, of course, place a still heavier burden on transport facilities as areas of exploitation will become still more distant from the main manufacturing districts. The timber industry provides one of the best illustrations of a major problem in Soviet economic geography, namely the great distance which often separates rich raw material resources from the districts in which they are required.

TEXTILE INDUSTRIES

The textile industry was one of the few branches of manufacturing which were at all well developed before the Revolution. Traditional domestic linen manufacture in the mixed forest zone of European Russia was succeeded, in the nineteenth century, by mechanized textile production, mainly of cotton, which was heavily concentrated in the Moscow basin. Cotton has remained by far the most important branch of textile manufacture in the U.S.S.R., though its predominance has slightly declined in recent years. Of all types of cloth produced, 75 per cent is still cotton, compared with 86 per cent in 1913.

The expansion of textile manufacture in the inter-war period was markedly less rapid than that of the heavier branches of industry. Between 1913 and 1940 output of all types of cloth increased by only half. Since the war, growth has accelerated and production in 1961 was more than double that of 1940. The output of cotton textiles has expanded less rapidly than that of other branches, the biggest growth has been achieved in the case of "silk", though it should be noted that this includes artificial fibres which now make up the bulk of production in this category.

TABLE 16. TEXTILE PRODUCTION, 1913–61

MILLIONS OF SQ M. FIGURES IN BRACKETS ARE INDEX NUMBERS
RELATING PRODUCTION TO THAT OF 1913

	1913	1940	1961
Cotton	1817 (100)	2704 (149)	4874 (268)
Woollen	138 (100)	152 (110)	454 (329)
Linen	121 (100)	268 (221)	493 (407)
"Silk"*	35 (100)	64 (183)	682 (1950)
Total	2111 (100)	3188 (151)	6503 (308)

* Includes artificial fibres.

Cotton

The production of cotton cloth is largely divorced from the main cotton-growing areas, a state of affairs which has persisted since the nineteenth century. The Russian Republic, which grows very little cotton, still produces some 85 per cent of the Soviet Union's cotton cloth, nearly 80 per cent of it in the Centre, much the same proportion as in 1913. Transcaucasia and Central Asia, the main cotton-producing districts, still have only a small share of the manufacturing. The great cotton towns of the Centre lie mainly to the north-east of Moscow, between the capital and the upper Volga. The industry is carried on in some 40 towns in this district, of which Ivanovo is by far the most important. Cotton manufacture also takes place in the north-west at Leningrad, Narva and Tallinn and, on a small scale, in a few towns of the Ukraine and Urals. Since the Revolution, new mills have been established at Leninakan, Kirovabad and Baku in Transcaucasia, at Tashkent, Fergana and Ashkhabad in Central Asia and at Barnaul in West Siberia. Current plans envisage further expansion of the industry in cotton-growing districts; even so the Centre is expected to continue producing two-thirds of the country's cotton cloth. One major advance has been achieved: whereas before the Revolution half the raw cotton was imported, the present, much larger industry is supplied entirely from internal resources.

Wool

Although the production of woollen cloth is more than three times that of 1913, the actual quantity is still less than one-tenth that of cotton. The woollen branch is rather more widely dispersed. The Centre is again the most important single region, but woollen textiles are also produced in a number of towns in the North-west, Belorussian, Black Earth Centre, Volga, Ural, Ukraine, Georgia and Central Asian regions.

Linen

Linen manufacture is, as might be expected, a speciality of the Centre and North-west. It is carried on in a number of towns of the cotton-manufacturing belt, where Kostroma is the leading producer, as well as in Belorussia and the Baltic republics.

Silk and Artificial Fibres

These are made in three regions, Central Asia and Transcaucasia (where the main product is natural silk), and the Centre, which accounts for over 70 per cent of the total and where production is almost entirely of artificial fibres.

It will be observed that the textile industry as a whole is heavily concentrated in the Centre, which is the dominant producer in all branches. Conversely, the industry is poorly represented in such major industrial areas as the Donbass, Urals and Kuzbass, where its introduction might well be encouraged in order to produce a more varied employment structure.

LIGHT INDUSTRY

No mention has so far been made of the production of consumer goods, the large-scale output of which is so marked a feature of the economies of western

FIG. 33. Distribution of mining and manufacturing industry. The numbers round the large circle at bottom right refer to the 11 industrial regions indicated on the map. (Based on a map by R. E. Lonsdale and J. H. Thompson, *Economic Geography*, **36**, no. 1, Jan. 1960, p. 42.)

Europe and North America. As has already been suggested, light industry has received a relatively small share of Soviet capital investment and output has risen much more slowly than in the case of the heavier branches. Over the past decade, however, rather more attention has been paid to the production of consumer goods. In 1964, to give a few examples, the U.S.S.R. produced 474 million pairs of leather footwear, nearly 5 million radio and 3 million television receivers, 3·8 million sewing machines, 2·9 million washing machines, 1·2 million refrigerators, 687,000 motor cycles and 29 million clocks and watches. All these figures are well above those of ten years ago, but in most cases are still a long way behind those of other industrially advanced powers. Perhaps the most striking example of all is that of motor car production which in 1964 was only 185,000, one for every 1200 people. The present situation is summed up by the fact that, in 1964, total Soviet industrial production was 7·8 per cent greater than in 1963, this increase involving a growth of more than 8 per cent in the output of "the means of production" (i.e. capital equipment) and a 6·5 per cent increase in the output of consumer goods. Although production of the latter is undoubtedly expanding more rapidly than ever before, the emphasis on heavy industry remains a major aspect of Soviet industrial development.

Industrial Regions (Fig. 33)

Soviet industry is a good deal less concentrated in its distribution than that of most European countries; consequently industrial regions are less easy to define. However, there are a number of areas which are major contributors to the industrial economy of the U.S.S.R. and may thus be recognized as industrial regions.

Nearly three-quarters of all Soviet industry is found in an area extending from the western frontier to the eastern flank of the Urals and within this zone there are five districts where industry is particularly concentrated. Two of these, the **Eastern Ukraine,** embracing the Dnepr bend and the Donbass, and the **Urals,** are major areas of heavy industry, concentrating their attention on mining, iron and steel, engineering and, to a lesser extent, the chemical industry. Both depend mainly on local resources of coal, iron ore and other metallic minerals, though the Urals, as we have seen, rely also on outside coal supplies. The remaining three regions are much more varied in their industrial structure. The **Moscow Basin,** which now contains nearly one-fifth of Soviet manufacturing industry, is mainly concerned with textiles, engineering, particularly the more highly skilled branches, and chemicals. This region accounts for a large proportion of the country's rather limited output of consumer goods. The Moscow basin owes its importance to its long industrial tradition, its reservoir of skilled labour and its position at the centre of communications rather than to local raw materials. The **Volga Region** is one of increasing industrial importance.

The major cities of the region are engaged in oil refining, food processing, engineering and chemical industries. The region owes its growing importance to recent rapid development of its resources of oil and hydroelectricity and to the function of the river itself as a major transport artery. The fifth industrial concentration in European Russia is the **Leningrad** district. Like the Moscow Basin, though on a much smaller scale, this area is concerned with a variety of highly skilled industrial activities, particularly the production of precision instruments and electrical equipment and is also important in the production of chemicals and textiles.

The five regions mentioned above now account for over 50 per cent of Soviet industrial production. A further 25 per cent is widely distributed among the cities of the European Plain. This leaves about one-quarter of Soviet industry scattered in small pockets over the whole of Siberia, Central Asia and the Caucasus. Only the **Kuzbass** and possibly the **Karaganda** district, with their coal-mining and metallurgical activities, can be considered as industrial regions of any significance and even these are small when compared with the major industrial concentrations of European Russia. Small centres of heavy industry are found, as we have seen, in the Baykal district, the Far East, Central Asia and the Caucasus, but these are of local rather than national importance. These districts also carry on a variety of other manufacturing industries but these are of minor significance to the industrial economy as a whole.

CHAPTER 10

TRANSPORT

In a country the size of the Soviet Union, economic development obviously involves the development of internal transport on a massive scale to permit the carriage of large volumes of raw materials and finished goods over long distances. As we have already seen, one of the major problems in the U.S.S.R. has been the construction of transport links to tap raw material resources in remote areas.

The relative importance of the various forms of transport is shown in the following figures.

TABLE 17. PRINCIPAL FORMS OF GOODS TRANSPORT WITHIN THE U.S.S.R. THOUSAND MILLION TON-KM. FIGURES IN BRACKETS INDICATE PERCENTAGE OF TOTAL GOODS TRAFFIC.

	1913	1940	1950	1961
Railway	76·4 (60·6)	415·0 (85·1)	602·3 (84·4)	1566·6 (78·4)
Inland waterway	28·9 (22·9)	36·1 (7·4)	46·2 (6·5)	106·0 (5·3)
Road	0·1 (0·1)	8·9 (1·8)	20·1 (2·8)	105·7 (5·3)
Sea	20·3 (16·1)	23·8 (4·9)	39·7 (5·6)	159·1 (8·0)
Air	— (—)	n (—)	0·1 (—)	0·6 (—)
Pipeline	0·3 (0·2)	3·8 (3·8)	4·9 (0·7)	60·0 (3·0)
Total	126·0 (100·0)	487·6 (100·0)	713·3 (100·0)	1998·0 (100·0)

TABLE 18. PRINCIPAL FORMS OF PASSENGER TRANSPORT WITHIN THE U.S.S.R. THOUSAND MILLION PASSENGER–KM. FIGURES IN BRACKETS INDICATE PERCENTAGE OF TOTAL PASSENGER TRAFFIC.

	1913	1940	1950	1961
Railway	30·3 (92·7)	98·0 (92·2)	88·0 (89·5)	176·3 (65·9)
Inland waterway	1·4 (4·3)	3·8 (3·6)	2·7 (2·8)	4·4 (1·6)
Road	— (—)	3·4 (3·2)	5·2 (5·3)	69·3 (25·9)
Sea	1·0 (3·0)	0·9 (0·8)	1·2 (1·2)	1·3 (0·5)
Air	— (—)	0·2 (0·2)	1·2 (1·2)	16·4 (6·1)
Total	32·7 (100·0)	106·3 (100·0)	98·3 (100·0)	267·7 (100·0)

Railways are by far the most important form of transport for both goods and passengers. Inland waterways come a very poor second as far as goods traffic is concerned and have recently been overtaken by roads, which are much more important passenger carriers. Road transport, though of rapidly increasing importance, is still of minor significance in most parts of the country: this is in vivid contrast to conditions in North America or western Europe. In the U.S.S.R., railways remain the lifelines of the economy in a very real sense and the network is still being expanded and improved. Indeed, between 1913 and 1940 the railways' share of goods and passenger traffic increased considerably and there was a marked decline in the proportion carried by sea and inland waterway. In the post-war years, the latter have continued to decline in relative importance and the railways' share of traffic has also diminished. Roads have gained rapidly since 1950, particularly in the case of passenger traffic. Pipelines are now a significant contributor to the transport of goods and airways carry a much larger share of passenger traffic than do waterways.

RAILWAYS

The Soviet régime inherited a fairly extensive network of 36,330 miles (58,500 km) and this has been more than doubled to reach 78,900 miles (127,100 km) in 1961. This may be compared with the United States' total of 224,000 miles (360,000 km) of railroad. The Soviet network is at its densest in the European part of the country, particularly to the west of the Volga (Fig. 34). There is a distinct radial pattern of trunk lines centred on Moscow and the heaviest concentration occurs in the eastern Ukraine, particularly in the Donbass. Beyond the Volga, the pattern is one of a few major trunk routes from which run numerous branch lines; only in the Ural region is there anything approaching a network. In addition to the many branches and short distance links which have been constructed since the Revolution, a number of trunk lines have also been built. The most important of these are the Turksib (Turkestan–Siberia) railway, which links Central Asia north-eastward to the Trans-Siberian, and the lines from the Urals south-eastward through Karaganda to join the Turksib. The Vorkuta railway, linking the Pechora coal-field to the European industrial areas has already been mentioned (p. 94). New rail links have also been built between the U.S.S.R. and China. The line from Ulan Ude through Ulan Bator, capital of the Mongolian Republic, to Tsining and thus to Peking was completed in 1955. A projected line from Central Asia through Sinkiang to reach Lanchow, in Kansu, is believed to be still under construction.

Probably even more important than the construction of new lines are the improvements which have been made to existing routes. Some 8 per cent of the network has been electrified and it is intended that a further 8 per cent shall be converted by 1965. Diesel traction is rapidly replacing steam on other routes and

Fig. 34. Railways.

it is hoped that, by 1965, 85 per cent of all goods traffic will be hauled by either diesel or electric locomotives. Another major development has been the double tracking of many formerly single-line routes. These improvements have been reflected in a vast increase in the volume of rail traffic which stands at twenty times its 1913 level in the case of goods and nearly six times in the case of passengers.

INLAND WATERWAYS

Rivers and canals have long been of great importance in the economic life of Russia and, although they now carry little more than 5 per cent of internal goods traffic compared with 23 per cent in 1913, the actual volume carried has increased more than threefold since the Revolution. In Asiatic Russia, north of the Trans-Siberian railway, the great rivers which flow to the Arctic are the main transport arteries for a vast area, but the volume of traffic which they carry is small and the European waterways are far more important (Fig. 35). The low relief of the European plain with its large, slow-flowing rivers whose headwaters are close to each other and separated by low watersheds, provides ideal conditions for water transport. As we saw in Chapter 3 the rivers were used as trading arteries in early times and some of the canals between them were built in the days of Peter the Great. A great deal of capital has been invested in canal construction and river improvement during the Soviet period. The most important system is that based on the Volga, which now carries two-thirds of all water-borne traffic. The upper Volga is joined through the Rybinsk reservoir and Lakes Onega and Ladoga to the Baltic and to Moscow via the Moscow canal. This system is linked to the White Sea by the White Sea–Baltic Canal and to the Black Sea by way of the recently-completed Volga–Don Canal. The Kama and its tributaries give access to the western flank of the Urals. The development of the Volga waterways has been a major achievement of the Soviet period. Apart from the actual building of the canals there has been much widening and deepening of rivers, particularly in the section between the upper Volga and the Baltic, where the Rybinsk reservoir serves as a regulating water body. Navigation improvements have often been accompanied by the installation of major hydroelectric plant, as for example at Kuybyshev and Volgograd and at Tsimlyansk on the Don. Many other rivers of European Russia are navigable over long distances, at least by small vessels, though none is comparable in importance to the Volga. The Dnepr has been much improved, particularly by the construction of the Zaporozh'ye and Kakhovka dams. The Dnepr is also joined, by a canal through the Poles'ye, to the Bug, a tributary of the Vistula.

One major drawback to the use of waterways throughout practically the whole of the Soviet Union is, of course, the winter freeze which lasts for periods ranging from four to six months according to latitude.

NAVIGABLE
WATERWAYS
OF
EUROPEAN
U.S.S.R.

Fɪɢ. 35. Inland waterways of European U.S.S.R. Canals and major hydro-electric stations are named in red.

SEA TRANSPORT

Quite apart from its importance in the foreign trade of the U.S.S.R., maritime transport also plays a significant role in the movement of goods from one part of the U.S.S.R. to another. In fact 50 per cent more "internal" goods traffic is carried by sea than by river and canal. Traffic is heaviest between the various ports on the Black Sea and across the Caspian, these routes working in con-

6

junction with the river and canal systems already mentioned. The Northern Sea Route through the Arctic Ocean serves as an outlet for the limited traffic of the Siberian rivers and is even used for trade with the Far Eastern Region, though it is only open in its entirety for ten or twelve weeks in the year. The Far East also depends to some extent on the lengthy sea route from the Black Sea via the Dardanelles and Suez Canal.

ROAD TRANSPORT

Road transport in the Soviet Union is still in the early stages of development, though considerable expansion has taken place in the post-war period. In 1940 the U.S.S.R. produced 145,400 motor vehicles of which only 5500 were cars. In 1964 output was 418,000 goods vehicles and 185,000 cars. While this increase in production denotes the establishment of a sizeable motor vehicle industry, the number of vehicles on the roads remains low, probably fewer than 5 million in the whole country. The road network remains rudimentary. Of 830,000 miles (1,340,000 km) of motor road in 1961, only 180,000 miles (290,000 km) were hard-surfaced and of these only 54,000 miles (87,000 km) had a cement or asphalt cover. This last figure, however, indicates considerable progress in the post-war years: in 1945 there were only 6400 miles (10,200 km) in this category. Obviously the network of main roads is a very open one, even in the European part of the country. In this part of the Soviet Union, most of the traffic is over quite short distances. Roads are much more important for long-distance traffic in areas where railways are not available, though the actual volume of traffic in such areas is small. Some of the biggest road-building projects in recent years have been concerned with such outlying regions. The Aldan Highway, for example, from Never (near the Manchurian frontier) to Yakutsk is one of several roads built to run northward from various points along the Trans-Siberian railway. There has also been a good deal of construction in Transcaucasia and Central Asia. During the past decade much attention has been paid to the improvement of major routes in the European part of the country while there are now a number of modern, well-surfaced main roads. Road transport, however, still carries little more than 5 per cent of Soviet goods traffic and generally serves to feed the railways. Passenger travel by road has increased twentyfold over its pre-war volume. The railways, which previously had a virtual monopoly of passenger transport, now account for some 65 per cent of passenger travel, the roads having increased their share to 25 per cent. While much of this increased road travel will be short-distance commuting into towns it does include a growing number of journeys by bus between the cities of European Russia.

AIR TRANSPORT

Aircraft at present play a negligible part in the movement of goods and are probably most important in remote parts of Siberia, where small consignments of valuable produce are carried by air. As a means of passenger transport, however, airways are of rapidly growing importance for long journeys. The U.S.S.R. now has a large network of internal air routes by which most major cities can be reached from Moscow within 12 hours.

CHAPTER 11

POPULATION

POPULATION GROWTH

Although a great deal of information concerning the population of the Russian Empire and the Soviet Union can be gathered from a variety of sources, it is difficult to present a concise summary of population growth, for a number of reasons. In the first place, only four complete censuses have ever been taken, in 1897, 1926, 1939 and 1959. For the period before 1897 and for years between the censuses, it is necessary to have recourse to various estimates and partial enumerations, the accuracy of which must always be open to some doubt. The profound effects on population growth of the war of 1914–17, the Revolution and its aftermath and the Second World War, together with the several major boundary revisions which have taken place during the past fifty years add to the problems involved. Nevertheless, it is possible to give at least a general picture of population growth and change since the early eighteenth century and this will provide, in many senses, a commentary on the historical and economic developments discussed in earlier chapters.

1724–1897

Some of the earliest population estimates available were made during the reign of Peter the Great. These do not cover the entire population within the Russian Empire as it then existed, but are concerned with the "Russian population" only, that is to say, with the whole population, regardless of ethnic origin, living in the European part of the territory under Peter's control, together with such Russians, Ukrainians and Belorussians as lived in the Asiatic part. Figures on this basis are available for 1724 and in Table 19 these are compared with the equivalent totals (i.e. covering the same areas and the same classes of people) for 1859 and 1897.

In addition to the rapid natural increase indicated by a population growth of more than 400 per cent in 173 years, these figures show a major redistribution of the Russian population over that period. Most striking is the movement from north to south in European Russia involving large-scale colonization of the steppe. Whereas in 1724 nearly two-thirds of the Russian population lived in the forested central and northern parts of the European plain, by 1897 this proportion had

126

TABLE 19. THE GROWTH AND DISTRIBUTION OF THE "RUSSIAN POPULATION", 1724–1897.

MILLIONS. FIGURES IN BRACKETS INDICATE PERCENTAGE OF TOTAL.

	1724	1859	1897	1897 as % of 1724
Total	17·9 (100·0)	58·6 (100·0)	94·3 (100·0)	527
European Russia	17·5 (97·8)	55·2 (94·2)	87·4 (92·7)	498
Centre and North	11·3 (63·2)	20·4 (34·8)	30·7 (32·6)	272
South*	6·2 (34·6)	34·8 (59·4)	56·7 (60·1)	915
Asiatic Russia	0·4 (2·2)	3·4 (5·8)	6·9 (7·3)	1725

*Essentially the European steppelands.

fallen to less than one-third. While the actual numbers living in the centre and north increased nearly threefold over the 173-year period, the population of the south rose to nearly nine times its 1724 level. Most of this redistribution took place before the middle of the nineteenth century, by which time most of the steppe had been brought under cultivation. The most rapid population increase occurred in the Asiatic part of the country which in 1724 contained only 400,000 settlers of European origin. This number had multiplied eightfold by 1859 and doubled again between 1859 and 1897. The proportion of the total Russian population living in Asia, however, remained small.

1897–1913

The total population of the Russian Empire in 1897 including all ethnic groups within its boundaries at that date, was 125·7 million. By 1913 this had risen to 165·7 million, an increase of 32 per cent in 16 years (Table 20).

TABLE 20. POPULATION OF THE RUSSIAN EMPIRE, 1897–1913.

MILLIONS. FIGURES IN BRACKETS INDICATE PERCENTAGE OF TOTAL.

	1897	1913	1913 as % of 1897
Total	125·7 (100·0)	165·7 (100·0)	132
European Russia	103·6 (82·4)	136·1 (82·1)	131
Siberia and Far East	7·2 (5·7)	10·0 (6·0)	139
Asiatic Steppe	2·5 (2·0)	4·0 (2·4)	160
Turkestan	7·5 (6·0)	9·6 (5·8)	128
Transcaucasia	4·9 (3·9)	6·0 (3·6)	122

During this short period, the distribution of the population among the major divisions of the country changed but little. The most rapid increases were in the Asiatic steppe region (the provinces of Ural'sk, Turgay, Akmolinsk and Semi-palatinsk, now part of Kazakhstan) and in Siberia and the Far East, these areas together increasing their population from 9·7 to 14 million. Growth in Turkestan and Transcaucasia on the other hand was appreciably below the national average. Although regional variations in the rate of natural increase may well have played some part in bringing about these differences, there can be little doubt that the main factor at work was migration from European Russia into Siberia. This movement had been in progress since the seventeenth century but remained on a small scale until the latter part of the nineteenth. Between 1800 and 1860, some 566,000 migrants settled in Asiatic Russia and of these at least 60 per cent were convicts or exiles. The liberation of the serfs in 1861 was followed by a rapid increase of peasant colonization in Siberia and in the next forty years more than 2 million people moved from Europe to Asia, an annual average more than five times that of the preceding period. Migration became still more rapid in the early part of the twentieth century, totalling 3 million between 1900 and 1914 and including only a small proportion of forced migrants. Thus, between the beginning of the nineteenth century and the outbreak of the First World War, some 5·5 million people moved from European Russia into the Asiatic parts of the Empire. In the areas most affected, namely Siberia and the Far East, the natives were soon outnumbered and the population became predominantly Russian. Russians and Ukrainians accounted for 85 per cent of the people of these regions as a whole and were in the majority in all parts except Yakutia and Kamchatka. In the Asiatic steppe, where the native population was more numerous, Russians and Ukrainians accounted for some 40 per cent of the 1914 total. Turkestan, on the other hand, received relatively few settlers: the 400,000 Russians and Ukrainians living in that region in 1914 amounted to only 6 per cent of the total.

1913–1926

The period between 1913 and the first Soviet census of 1926 was one of great internal upheaval and thus of confusion as regards the details of population growth. The 1926 census revealed a total of 147 million people within the frontiers of the U.S.S.R. as they were at that date, 18·7 million less than the figure for the Russian Empire in 1913. It should be remembered, however, that in the intervening period the Soviet Union had lost control of Finland, the Baltic States, Poland and other western territories with a total 1913 population of 26·4 million. Thus the figure which should be compared with the 1926 total is 139·3 million (165·7—26·4) indicating a growth of 7·7 million or 5·6 per cent in the thirteen-year period. Such an increase was a good deal less rapid than the pre-war average, an obvious result of the special events of the period. Had pre-war rates of increase been maintained, the 1926 population should have been at least 175 million, 28 million more than was in fact the case. The allocation of this "population deficit" to its various causes is a complicated process and many different views have been expressed. The most likely suggestion is as follows: emigration 2 million, military deaths in the First World War 2 million, deaths in the civil war, epidemics and famine 14 million, deficit of births due to reduced fertility during this period 10 million.

1926–1939

In the years between the 1926 census and that of 1939 there were no significant changes in the boundaries of the U.S.S.R. and the results are therefore strictly comparable. Over this period of thirteen years, the Soviet population rose from 147 to 170·5 million, an increase of 16 per cent. This represents a rate of growth nearly three times as rapid as that for the period 1913-26 but still well below the rate for 1897–1913, reflecting slow natural increase in the difficult years of the late 1920's and early 30's. Once again, migration from European to Asiatic areas was an outstanding feature (Table 21).

TABLE 21. POPULATION OF THE U.S.S.R., 1926–39.

MILLIONS. FIGURES IN BRACKETS INDICATE PERCENTAGE OF TOTAL.

	1926	1939	1939 as % of 1926
Total	147·0 (100·0)	170·5 (100·0)	116
European U.S.S.R.	114·3 (77·7)	129·3 (75·8)	113
Siberia and Far East	12·5 (8·5)	16·6 (9·7)	133
Central Asia	7·6 (5·2)	10·5 (6·2)	138
Kazakhstan	6·1 (4·1)	6·1 (3·6)	100
Transcaucasia	6·6 (4·5)	8·0 (4·7)	121

Rates of growth well above the national average were recorded in Central Asia and Transcaucasia as well as in Siberia and the Far East. In the former, essentially non-Russian areas, declining death rates as well as an appreciable migration from European areas were responsible for the rapid growth while in Siberia and the Far East migration gain was the dominant factor. Between 1926 and 1939 there was a net migration gain of 1·2 million in the Ural region, 1·2 million in Siberia and 900,000 in the Far East.

1939–1959

The census of 1939 was followed, in 1940, by the addition of large territories in the west which raised the population of the U.S.S.R. by more than 20 million to a total of 192·6 million* and it is with the latter figure that post-war data must be compared. The situation immediately following the Second World War is very obscure and a number of conflicting estimates have been made for 1945–46. The lowest of these puts the 1945 population at only 173 million, 20 million below that of 1940. Had pre-war increase rates continued through the war years, the population would have reached at least 203 million in 1945, suggesting a wartime population deficit of some 30 million. When we consider that military deaths, at a conservative estimate, numbered at least 5 million, that civilian losses were probably even greater and that high mortality and low fertility must have affected the whole population during the war years, this estimate appears not at all unreasonable. Furthermore, if the 1945 estimate of 173 million is accepted, then the 1959 census total of 208·8 million indicates an increase of 21 per cent in fourteen years. This would seem to be a likely rate of growth in the post-war period in view of official birth-rate and death-rate figures which show a natural increase above 1·5 per cent per annum.

Whatever confusion may exist concerning the events of the 1940's, the 1959 census figure of 208·8 million may be taken as having a high degree of accuracy. It indicates a population growth of only 8·4 per cent in the twenty years since 1939, comprising an actual decline during the war and an accelerated increase in the post-war period. For comparison with earlier years, a simplified regional breakdown of the census figures is given in Table 22, while Table 23 provides a more detailed picture.

TABLE 22. POPULATION OF THE U.S.S.R. 1939–59.

MILLIONS. FIGURES IN BRACKETS INDICATE PERCENTAGE OF TOTAL.

	1939*	1959	1959 as % of 1939
Total	192·6 (100·0)	208·8 (100·0)	108·4
European U.S.S.R.	151·4 (78·6)	152·8 (73·2)	100·9
Siberia and Far East	16·6 (8·6)	23·5 (11·3)	141·6
Central Asia	10·5 (5·4)	13·7 (6·6)	130·5
Kazakhstan	6·1 (3·2)	9·3 (4·4)	152·6
Transcaucasia	8·0 (4·2)	9·5 (4·5)	118·8

* 1959 boundaries.

* This is the 1939 population of the U.S.S.R. within its 1959 frontiers. The latter are not exactly the same as those of 1940 (see Chapter 3) and the 1940 population within the 1940 frontiers was in fact 190·7 million.

TABLE 23. POPULATION OF THE U.S.S.R., ECONOMIC REGIONS* AND REPUBLICS, 1939–59.

THOUSANDS. FIGURES IN BRACKETS INDICATE PERCENTAGE OF TOTAL.

	1939	1959	1959 as % of 1939
U.S.S.R.	192,577 (100·0)	208,827 (100·0)	108·4
R.S.F.S.R.	109,379 (56·8)	117,534 (56·3)	107·4
North-west	12,169 (6·3)	11,474 (5·5)	94·2
Centre	25,308 (13·1)	24,789 (11·9)	97·9
Volga-Vyatka	8,698 (4·5)	8,253 (4·0)	94·8
Central Black Earth	10,439 (5·4)	8,698 (4·2)	83·2
Volga	12,125 (6·3)	12,454 (6·0)	102·7
North Caucasus	10,512 (5·5)	11,785 (5·6)	112·1
Ural	14,444 (7·5)	18,613 (8·9)	128·8
West Siberia	7,937 (4·1)	10,159 (4·9)	128·0
East Siberia	5,185 (2·7)	6,960 (3·3)	134·2
Far East	2,562 (1·3)	4,347 (2·1)	169·7
Ukraine	41,368 (21·5)	41,869 (20·0)	101·2
Donetz–Dnepr	14,760 (7·7)	16,548 (7·9)	112·1
South-west	21,756 (11·3)	20,255 (9·7)	93·1
South	4,852 (2·5)	5,066 (2·4)	104·4
Lithuania	2,880 (1·5)	2,711 (1·3)	94·1
Latvia	1,885 (1·0)	2,093 (1·0)	111·0
Estonia	1,052 (0·5)	1,197 (0·6)	113·8
Georgia	3,540 (1·8)	4,044 (1·9)	114·2
Azerbaijan	3,205 (1·7)	3,698 (1·8)	115·4
Armenia	1,282 (0·7)	1,763 (0·8)	137·5
Uzbekistan	6,336 (3·3)	8,106 (3·9)	127·9
Kirgiziya	1,458 (0·8)	2,066 (1·0)	141·7
Tadzhikstan	1,484 (0·8)	1,980 (0·9)	133·4
Turkmeniya	1,252 (0·7)	1,516 (0·7)	121·1
Kazakhstan	6,094 (3·2)	9,310 (4·5)	152·8
Belorussia	8,910 (4·6)	8,054 (3·9)	90·4
Moldavia	2,452 (1·3)	2,884 (1·4)	117·6

* For the boundaries of these regions see Fig. 17B.

These figures reveal striking contrasts between the various economic regions. The population within the present boundaries of the U.S.S.R. increased by 8·4 per cent between 1939 and 1959. The majority of economic regions in the European part of the country experienced population growth below this national average, exceptions being the north Caucasus, Ural and Donetz–Dnepr regions and the Moldavian, Latvian and Estonian republics. An actual decline occurred in the North-west, Centre, Central Black Earth, Volga–Vyatka and South-west regions and in Belorussia and Lithuania. The Urals, West Siberia, East Siberia and the Far East, in contrast, all recorded increases well above the national average at 29, 28, 34 and 70 per cent respectively, as did Kazakhstan (53 per

FIG. 36. Total population change, 1939–59. Areas of decline in red.

FIG. 37. Rural population change, 1939–59. Areas of decline in red.

cent) the Central Asian republics (30 per cent) and Transcaucasia (19 per cent). Differences in the rate of natural increase no doubt played their part and it seems likely that fertility is above average in areas of colonization, such as Siberia, which have a high proportion of young adults, and in the non-Russian areas of Transcaucasia and Central Asia. At the same time there can be little doubt that migration movements have played a major role in determining regional rates of population growth, these movements involving migration from rural to urban areas throughout the Soviet Union as well as from the European to the Asiatic parts of the country.

A good deal more detail is provided by the maps of population change (Figs. 36–38) on pages 132 and 133. From these it will be seen that, whereas in practically every part of the country urban populations have increased during the twenty-year period, rural numbers have declined over a very wide area. Consequently there are many similarities between the map of total population change (Fig. 36) and that showing the strength of the urban element (Fig. 39). Areas with the most rapid rates of growth between 1939 and 1959 tend also to be those with high proportions of town-dwellers at the latter date. The map of total population change (Fig. 36) shows a large area of actual decline stretching from the western frontier to the upper Volga and from Leningrad well into the

FIG. 38. Urban population change, 1939–59. Areas of decline in red.

A Geography of the Soviet Union

northern Ukraine. Islands of population increase within this zone are generally oblasts within which major cities are to be found, Minsk, Kiyev and the Moscow–Gor'kiy areas being cases in point. Over the remainder of the area, quite apart from wartime losses, which would in any case be expected to give below-average rates of increase, rural depopulation has reached a large enough scale to cause an actual decline in numbers, despite the growth of urban centres. Increases in the western republics of Estonia and Latvia reflect the immigration of Russians who, living mainly in the towns, now make up some 20 per cent of the total population.

Rapid increase has taken place in parts of the eastern Ukraine (Donetskaya Oblast 37 per cent) where urban growth in a major industrial area has been the main factor at work. In the southern Ukraine, growth has been a good deal less rapid and rural populations have declined. The Volga region shows a good deal of variation. Rural populations have decreased throughout the region, resulting in a decline in total numbers. There has been slow growth in the south and rapid increase (37 per cent) in the Kuybyshevskaya Oblast'. With the exception of the small Checheno-Ingushskaya and Yugo-Osetinskaya (South Osetin) areas, the Caucasus and Transcaucasia have increased their populations, the most rapid growth occurring in Armenia and particularly in the capital, Yerevan.

Fig. 39. Urban population as a percentage of total population, 1959. The boundaries of all S.S.R.'s, A.S.S.R.'s, A.Ob.'s and N.O.'s are shown.

Kazakhstan and Central Asia are in contrast to the areas mentioned so far, in that they have experienced a growth of rural as well as urban populations. In northern Kazakhstan, those oblasts which have a share of the virgin lands show very rapid increase in total population, reaching more than 100 per cent in Pavlodar, while the expansion of the Karaganda industrial complex accounts for most of the 150 per cent increase in that oblast. In the southern parts of Central Asia, growth has been rapid in all but the most remote mountain areas, Tyan'-Shan'skaya Oblast' Gorno-Badakhshanskaya Avtonomnaya Oblast', the biggest increases occurring where there are major cities such as Tashkent, Dzhambul, Frunze and Alma-Ata, though rural areas, too, show significant growth.

Some of the most rapid percentage increases have taken place in north European Russia and northern Siberia, where several areas have more than doubled their population. In most cases, however, the actual numbers involved are small, though mention should be made of the Komi A.S.S.R., where there has been an increase from 319,000 to 806,000 due, mainly, to the opening up of the Vorkuta coal-field. The biggest numerical increases have, of course, occurred in southern parts of Siberia and the Far East. Although in several cases these have involved a growth in rural populations, urban growth is again the most significant aspect.

POPULATION DISTRIBUTION AND DENSITY

Despite the changes in distribution outlined in preceding paragraphs, the population of the U.S.S.R. remains heavily concentrated in the European part of the country. Siberia* and the Far East, which together account for almost half the total area have only about 21 million inhabitants, just over 10 per cent of the population. Kazakhstan, the Central Asian republics and Transcaucasia cover about 20 per cent of the territory and have a combined population of 32 million, 15 per cent of the total. This leaves some 75 per cent of the population, about 155 million people, in the European part of the country.

The map of population density (Fig. 40) serves to emphasize this uneven distribution. The average density for the country as a whole in 1962 was 9·9 per sq km (25·6 per sq mile) and areas with densities above this average are shown on the map by shading systems using unbroken lines. Such areas are clearly confined to two distinct zones. By far the larger of these embraces the whole of European U.S.S.R. south of the latitude of Leningrad, extending eastward across the Urals to the Kuzbass and southward into Transcaucasia. A much smaller area of above-average densities occurs in the foothill and basin zone of Soviet Central Asia. Areas with densities above 40 per sq km (104 per

* Excluding the Kurgan and Tyumen' Oblasts, now part of the Ural region (see Fig. 17B).

FIG. 40. Population density, 1 January, 1962. Unbroken shadings denote areas with densities above the national average; broken lines and dots denote below-average densities.

sq mile), four times the Soviet average but still well below much of western Europe, are much more restricted in extent. The largest of these high-density regions covers virtually the whole of the Ukraine. Others include Moscow and oblasts along the Volga to the east of the capital, Leningradskaya Oblast', Lithuania and parts of Belorussia, much of the Caucasus and Transcaucasia and small parts of Central Asia. At the other end of the scale, much of Kazakhstan, north European Russia, Siberia and the Far East have densities below 5 per sq km (13 per sq mile), falling over large areas below 1 per sq km (2·6 per sq mile).

Although Fig. 40 makes no distinction between urban and rural populations, showing simply the density of population as a whole, its general pattern closely reflects the distribution and quality of agricultural land as described in Chapter 6. The zones of above-average population density correspond quite closely to the *Main Agricultural Belt* (zone II) and the *Southern Areas of High Agricultural Value* (zone IV) on the map of agricultural regions (p. 71). It is, of course, true that some of the highest oblast densities reflect the presence of major urban agglomerations but since oblast boundaries are designed to include a strong urban element in each case, differences in the degree of urbanization between oblasts are less great than might be expected. This, together with the fact that half the Soviet population still lives outside the towns results in a fairly close correspondence between the pattern of rural densities and that of overall density.

Urbanization

An increase in the urban element has been a characteristic of population change throughout the present century. Whereas in 1913 only 18 per cent lived in urban areas, this proportion had reached 51 per cent by 1962. In the latter year there were 113·4 million town-dwellers, 3·7 times as many as in 1913, and 108·1 million rural population, 80 per cent of the 1913 figure. The distribution of urban centres by size in 1962 was as follows:

TABLE 24. URBAN CENTRES WITH OVER 50,000 INHABITANTS.
SIZE GROUPS 1962

Over 1 million	6
500,000–1,000,000	21
250,000– 500,000	37
100,000– 250,000	110
50,000– 100,000	152
	326

The location of these 326 urban centres is shown in Fig. 41. Moscow, with 6·3 million inhabitants stands well above all other Soviet cities in size and is

TOWNS WITH OVER
50,000 INHABITANTS
JANUARY 1ST 1962

OVER 1,000,000
500,000 – 1,000,000
250,000 – 500,000
100,000 – 250,000
50,000 – 100,000

HALF SCALE

0   50 100 200 300 MILES
0 100 200 300 KMS.

Fig. 41. The 326 towns with populations over 50,000 on 1 January, 1962.

followed by Leningrad (3·5 million*) and Kiyev (1·2 million). The remaining "million" cities, which have only recently entered this class are Baku (1·1 million*), Gor'kiy (1·1 million*) and Tashkent (1·0 million). Cities of 500,000 to 1 million include the capitals of several republics (Tbilisi, Riga, Minsk, Yerevan, Alma-Ata) and numerous industrial and regional centres in the Ukraine (Donetsk, Dnepropetrovsk, Odessa, Kharkov, Voronezh) the Urals (Sverdlovsk, Chelyabinsk, Perm', Ufa), the Volga region (Kuybyshev, Kazan', Volgograd, Saratov) and West Siberia (Novosibirsk, Omsk). The remaining centres of more than 100,000 tend to show a concentration in the main industrial regions, while those in the 50–100,000 group are either small industrial centres or regional centres in the more remote parts of the country.

The proportion of the population living in urban areas is shown in detail in Fig. 39, where it will be seen that, apart from the expected high figures in the major industrial districts, the most striking feature is the below-average size of the urban element over much of the European part of the country. In this zone, rural populations, though declining, are still large, while at the same time urban populations have, with a few exceptions, grown relatively little during the past twenty years.

Despite the large-scale movement of population from rural to urban areas which has taken place over the last fifty years, the U.S.S.R. still has an appreciably smaller proportion of town-dwellers than is usually associated with a major industrial power and the agricultural labour force remains very large. In 1961, of a total working population of 78 millions, more than 43 per cent (34 million) were engaged in the agricultural sector of the economy as against 29 per cent (23 million) in extractive and manufacturing industry and 28 per cent in other occupations. These figures probably underestimate the proportion of the population directly or indirectly dependent on farming for a livelihood. One of the major unsolved problems of Soviet planning is that of accelerating the movement of population from agriculture into industry.

Forty-six per cent of the Soviet labour force (including 58 per cent of those employed in agriculture) are women. This widespread use of female labour reflects an overall labour shortage which is due in part to the inefficient use of a large number of workers in agriculture and in part to the heavy losses suffered during the Second World War. The effects of the war, together with a number of other factors, are illustrated by the age–sex data shown in Fig. 42. The Soviet population shows a large excess of females over males, the former numbering 114·8 million and the latter 94 million in 1959, a ratio of 82 males to every 100 females. This unbalance is visible in all age groups except those born since 1945, reaching its maximum among those born between 1909 and 1928, most of whom were of military age during the Second World War. Among the population aged 30–40 in 1959 there were only 75 men per 100 women and in the 40–50

* Including suburbs.

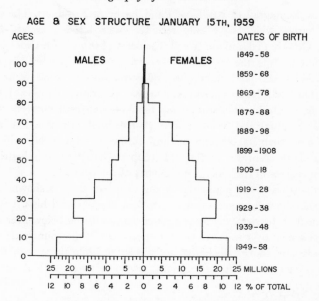

FIG. 42. The age and sex composition of the Soviet population.

age group only 62. The low birth-rate of the war years is reflected in the small numbers of both sexes in the 10–20 age group, while the large numbers of children below the age of 10 is a result of the accelerated population growth of the post-war period. As might be expected, the Soviet population is now a youthful one with 78 million people (34 per cent) below 20 years of age and no fewer than 46 million (23 per cent) below 10. The death rate, which in 1913 stood at 30·2 per 1000, has been reduced to 7·2 per 1000, one of the lowest in the world. The birth rate, at 23·8 per 1000, is also well below the 1913 level (47·0). The result is a natural increase of 16·6 per 1000 (1·66 per cent) per annum. In this respect, as in so many others, the U.S.S.R. occupies an intermediate position between the under-developed countries, whose rates of population growth are generally a good deal higher, and the advanced industrial countries where the increase is a good deal less rapid. With little or no likelihood of the death rate being further reduced and with the birth rate continuing to decline, albeit very slowly, the Soviet population is unlikely to increase more rapidly than it is doing at the moment. Consequently, there should be little difficulty in maintaining economic expansion at a rate more rapid than that of population growth in the foreseeable future. The major problems will be those of maintaining the rate of migration to the Asiatic parts of the country where the biggest untapped resources are now to be found, and of accelerating the movement of labour from agricultural to industrial activities.

FURTHER READING

BARANSKY, N. N., *Economic Geography of the Soviet Union*, Foreign Languages Publishing House, Moscow, 1956.

BERG, L. S., *The Natural Regions of the U.S.S.R.*, Macmillan, New York, 1950.

COLE, J. P., and GERMAN, F. C., *A Geography of the U.S.S.R.—The Background to a Planned Economy*, Butterworth, London, 1961.

CRESSEY, G. B., *Soviet Potentials—A Geographical Appraisal*, Syracuse University Press, 1962.

EAST, W. G., and MOODIE, A. E. (Eds.), *The Changing World*, Harrap, London, 1956 (chapters xiv–xviii).

GEORGE, P., *U.S.S.R., Haute Asie, Iran*, Presses Universitaires de France, Paris, 1947.

GRAY, G. D. B., *Soviet Land*, Black, London, 1957.

GREGORY, J. S., and SHAVE, D. W., *The U.S.S.R.—A Geographical Survey*, Harrap, London, 1944.

GREGORY, J. S., *Land of the Soviets*, Penguin Books, 1946.

HODGKINS, J. A., *Soviet Power—Energy Resources, Production and Potentials*, Prentice-Hall, London, 1961.

HOOSON, D. J. M., *A New Soviet Heartland?*, Van Nostrand, Princeton, N.J., 1964.

JORRÉ, G., *The Soviet Union—The Land and its People*, Translated and revised by E. D. Laborde, Longmans, London, 1961.

LORIMER, F., *The Population of the Soviet Union—History and Prospects*, League of Nations, Geneva, 1946.

LYDOLPH, P. E., *Geography of the U.S.S.R.*, Wiley, New York, 1964.

MELLOR, R. E. H., *Geography of the U.S.S.R.*, Macmillan, London, 1964.

MIROV, N. T., *Geography of Russia*, Wiley, New York, 1951.

NALIVKIN, D. V., *The Geology of the U.S.S.R.*, Pergamon Press, 1960.

OXFORD REGIONAL ECONOMIC ATLAS, The U.S.S.R. and Eastern Europe, Oxford University Press, 1956.

SHABAD, T., *The Geography of the U.S.S.R.*, Columbia University Press, New York, 1951.

SHIMKIN, D. B., *Minerals, a Key to Soviet Power*, Harvard University Press, 1953.

SUSLOV, S. P., *Physical Geography of Asiatic Russia*, Freeman, San Francisco, 1961.

THIEL, E., *The Soviet Far East*, Methuen, London, 1957.

INDEX

Numbers in **bold** *following page references denote figure references.*

143

DATE DUE
